BETSY'S NAPOLEON

BETSY'S NAPOLEON

by

JEANETTE EATON

Illustrated by

Pierre Brissaud

j

WILLIAM MORROW AND COMPANY

NEW YORK   1936

TO

E. E.

"Monte, monte, petit écureuil!"

CONTENTS

ILLUSTRATIONS

BETSY'S NAPOLEON

1

"BONEY WILL GET YOU!"

For years afterward she remembered it. Even in her gay twenties when life was just one ball after another, Elizabeth would often find herself thinking of the time she first heard of him. This recollection was most certain on her birthday. For she was just six years old to the minute when his name—his terrible, fateful name—was hurled at her out of the unknown.

About a year before the memorable date the whole family had come to live on the island of St. Helena. For Elizabeth's father, Mr. William Balcombe, had been sent from England by the famous private trading firm called The British East India Company to take charge of public sales at this station far off the coast of Africa.

The strange place hardly yet seemed home. Indeed, on that particular anniversary Elizabeth wished harder than ever that they were all back at Granny's house in England where they had been so happy. The day was dark and rainy and every gay plan had to be postponed. At the tea hour, however, things cheered up considerably. The table was graced by a birthday cake and strewn with gifts for the fortunate six-year-old. After tea her mother went to the pianoforte and played some of the favorite songs of that era, an old carol and then *Sally in Our Alley* and *The Wearing of the Green*.

Alas, all too soon came an end to the fun in the shape of old black Sarah, ready to take Betsy to bed. In wild rebellion, she shouted, "Go away! Go away! I'm not coming yet! I won't come!"

But those strong, relentless arms, which snatched her up, yielded to none of her struggles and kicks. While the treacherous family sat there smiling and unprotesting, Betsy was borne upstairs and set firmly down in her own room. As she began to unfasten buttons and ribbons, old Sarah proceeded to speak her mind.

"Why you naughty, Miss Betsy? On a birthday, too! Don't you know what happens to little English gals when they not good?"

The funny, kind, black face had taken on an expression which the child had never seen before. Reproof in it was familiar enough. But now it was stamped with a look of dread and awe. Thrilled with a sense of foreboding, Betsy whispered, "Tell me what happens!"

Then it was, in a tone she always remembered as terrible, Betsy learned the name which even at that moment was on a million lips throughout the civilized world. "Boney will get you!" cried the old woman.

It had a frightful sound. Shivering, Betsy managed to ask, "Who is Boney?"

"Boney? Why, Napoleon Bonaparte. Has your father nevah narrated about Boney? He is devil, horned devil on earth. Kings bow knee to him. Lightning is in his eye and

[4]

thrones fall down when he speak. His cannons roar day and night. He see enemy thousand miles away. So watch! You naughty?—Ovah he come in big schooner—ovah to St. Helena he come and tear you limb from limb. That king devil is Napoleon Bonaparte."

That night Betsy's dreams were haunted by the image of this fearful being. With eyes of flame, a horned head, one hand grasping a huge sword, the creature was half man, half monster. Even next day when she drowsily unclosed her eyes, the evil shape appeared. But it vanished at once. Somewhere outside in the garden she heard a gay voice calling to her, "Betsy, do get up! Picnic today, lazy bones!"

Up sprang Betsy then to a morning of brilliant sunshine. Looking down from the window ledge through a thicket of lac trees and tall pomegranates, she saw Jane, her elder sister, standing with merry face upturned. What a lovely world it was! Dew on the great white roses and on the glistening tips of the little pines. No room for horrid images. With a shout of glee, the child waved her hand and turned to hurry with her bath and dressing.

This was the real birthday—a second celebration. Immediately after breakfast she took her first ride. While her father walked beside her to show her how to sit and hold the reins, she rode proudly up and down the turfy avenue under the banyan trees. Whenever they turned about to repeat the performance, Betsy would look down into her father's sparkling hazel eyes and say, "Is he really mine— this beautiful white pony?"

"Yes, he is really yours—as long as you are good. I had him sent all the way from Capetown."

Luncheon was a picnic excursion up to Diana's Peak. Everyone went except baby Frank who was left at home with black Sarah and his nurse. Mrs. Balcombe, Betsy and Jane rode in a carriage. It was loaned, as she afterwards learned, by the kind Governor's wife. Her father rode ahead on his sturdy little mare. But Toby, the old Malay slave, had to walk and carry on his back a big basket of provisions.

As the carriage, drawn by two white oxen, lumbered up the steep, rough trails, Elizabeth was terrified by the deep ravines yawning beside the narrow road and hid her head in her mother's lap. She felt safer when they got out to walk up the path to the grassy slopes of the towering peak. Once in the open, she was thrilled by the view of the brilliant sea which curled white against the foot of the cliffs.

She was always astonished when the sea looked blue. For she still vividly remembered its unchanging gray during all those long weeks of the voyage from England. How the wind had howled in the rigging! Ever since she had hated wind and here at St. Helena it was often terrible. When she walked about Jamestown with her mother she sometimes had to bend almost double to keep her feet against it. But today, for once, the weather was perfect.

While luncheon was spread she and Jane climbed high up on the mountain side. Never before had Elizabeth been so far from home. Never had she been high enough for a view. She was fearfully excited to find out what the

[6]

country was like and was glad Jane could point everything out.

"Oh, Betsy," exclaimed her sister, "isn't it wonderful
to see the ocean in so many different places? Now St.
Helena *does* look like an island. If we could only get a
glimpse of Jamestown and the bay—yes, and of Plantation House! But these big peaks cut off the view."

In silence the younger child gazed about her. She
would never have known where she was. As Jane said,
those familiar landmarks—the village and the Governor's
big white house where he always lived in summer—must
be hiding behind the mountains.

It was a somber, jagged landscape, magnificent and
weird. Bare, rocky ridges rose steeply one after another
above dark valleys. Against the violet and buff tones of
the glistening rocks were splashed red and orange patches
of sun-baked clay. Far beyond the cactus and scrub
growth, dark patches of woods were topped by spiky
points of palms and the silver flutter of tall gum trees.
Yet such verdure seemed only to intensify the vast and
untamed desolation.

"Well," cried Jane impatiently, "don't you think it is
wonderful?"

Elizabeth shook her head. Every moment she stood here
she felt more and more lonely. Somehow she had expected
to find smooth, green hills, groves and flowers as there
were in England. Even her father, who now came bound-
ing up to call them to luncheon, had no magic to make
the view seem pleasing. He spun her about to look down
the other side of the mountain. But, although it was less
wild on that side, it was more melancholy.

[7]

"Right below is Longwood," said Mr. Balcombe, "the largest level plain on the island. That old farm house is used by the Lieutenant Governor sometimes as a summer residence. But much of the land has been planted in potatoes by the East India Company to sell to its own ships. They stop at St. Helena, you know, because it is on the direct trade route from China and India to England. Now, little girl, what do you think of Longwood?"

How bare it was! Even the few scrawny trees had been pushed into queer shapes by the great winds. Betsy shivered to think of any place so bleak and lonely. Suddenly she recalled what old Sarah had said the night before. What if that devil came over to punish her for mischief! He might snatch her from her lovely garden and fly with her up to that ugly plateau where no flowers grew. Why did it make her think of that dreadful Boney?

At that instant upon the open fields of Longwood fell the dark shadow of a cloud. It was shaped like a great, gray bird with ragged wings spread out to hide the sunlight. "Oh, look!" screamed Betsy in unreasoning terror. "What is that? Don't let him get me! Please don't!" She pressed close against her father's shiny riding boots.

Mr. Balcombe swung her up in his arms. "Silly baby, what did you think you saw? I have a little goose for a six-year-old daughter—afraid of a shadow!" When his tickling fingers finally made her laugh, he set her on her feet, snatched her hand, and, with Jane flying after, they raced down hill to the jolly picnic table.

Afterwards, on the way home, Betsy had another impression of St. Helena. At a certain point her father made her get out of the carriage with Jane and climb up a

[8]

vantage point overlooking the valley. Suddenly far below she saw a lovely wooded spot with long, low buildings in the middle of it. She was reminded of her mother's shell locket set with an emerald—so jeweled was the greenness against the brown precipices.

"Oh, how pretty!" she exclaimed. "What is that place?"

"Why, Betsy Balcombe," derided her sister, "don't you know your own home? That is the Briars. I can even see the window of your room."

As Betsy peered down, trying to realize that the tiny doll's house so far beneath was really the spacious, two-story bungalow in which she lived, her father asked her teasingly, "How many oranges can you count on our trees down there, my pretty?"

The child laughed, delighted with his joke. Her father was always promising that the glossy young trees he had set out in the garden were going to bear. But so far no fruit was to be seen even when she was right on the spot, let alone at such a distance. Yet to look down from this height past all the barren rocks made her suddenly glad for the beautiful Briars, so sheltered and serene, with flowers, grass and trees, a waterfall and a beautiful pool where golden fish swam in the hot sunshine.

Not once again that day did anything remind the little girl of the demon named Boney. But she by no means forgot him. Indeed, she had a morbid longing to hear more about him, yet dreaded to inquire further. Since black Sarah did not repeat her threat, Betsy's imagination was left alone to play with the horror. This it was apt to do just before she entered the shadowland of sleep.

During the lusty hours of the day she was far too happy

[9]

to give the awful creature a thought. And, indeed, although she was convinced of his existence, it never occurred to her that he walked about in ordinary flesh. The inconsistency at last brought her a fresh shock. And the force of it indelibly imprinted another scene from childhood on the soul of Betsy Balcombe.

At that time she must have been nearly eight years old, and one of the busiest children in the whole British Empire. True, most of this activity was play, trimmed with considerable mischief. But also she was learning many things—how to make a raisin pudding under cook's direction, how to sew a seam and read music and ride her spirited pony. Lately, moreover, she had lessons every morning with Miss Breen, the governess. Compared to games or the endless joy of watching the waterfall, work in the schoolroom was tiresome. But worst of all was having to curtsey and make polite remarks to the grown-ups who were always coming to call or dine at the Briars.

Among them quite often were strangers on shore from one of the big ships, anchored in the harbor to take on water and supplies. Perhaps the visitor might be an official of the East India Company or a British officer returning to India after home leave. In Betsy's opinion even these gentlemen were not worth attention. It was far more fun to chat with Peter out at the stables while he groomed the horses.

One evening, however, something which a visitor said exploded like a rocket in her brain. The flash of it lit up every detail of the occasion. It was stamped on her memory that she and Jane, who never saw half enough of their father, had expected that night to dine alone with him. For, due to the arrival of baby Alexander, Mrs. Balcombe was still having dinner in bed. Then they were told that since a visitor had appeared, they would have supper upstairs and must go and bid their father good night.

As Betsy sulkily followed Jane into the drawing-room, she saw a tall man standing at its far end. The candle light shone upon his large, beaked nose and he had a voice to correspond in size. So earnestly was he engaged in talk, that neither he nor Mr. Balcombe observed the shy entrance of the little girls. Betsy, always the bolder of the two, drew slowly nearer until she could perch on the carved arm of the bar-backed sofa almost under the stranger's elbow.

It was an active elbow. For, although the hand belonging to it was thrust into the pocket of white satin breeches, the arm jerked this way and that in response to the gesticulations of its mate. Years later by dipping into history, Elizabeth was able to reconstruct the rapid speech he flung at his companion.

"I tell you, Balcombe," the stranger was saying loudly, "Lord Castlercagh is in the right about it. England has no choice whatsoever about strongly opposing this usurper. He means to rule the world. Has not Holland become part of the French Empire? And now, think of this marriage to an Austrian Princess of the Blood! It makes the upstart stronger than ever. No wonder rumor has it that again he plans an invasion of England."

Those last words uttered in a tone of desperation transfixed the child on the sofa arm. England! Why, that was their homeland, where Granny lived still! That was a place of shady lanes and hedgerows and violets. Was anything going to happen to that beloved country? Intently she listened to her father's answer. She could see only his profile beyond the visitor's shoulder. Yet it reassured her and his voice dropped deep to draw up calm.

"Surely, sir, it is mere talk. Nelson laid that ghost nearly five years ago. The Emperor has few ships now, no men to spare for such an undertaking. Besides, Sir Arthur—or rather Lord Wellington—keeps too much of the French army busy in Spain. On the other hand, England may well regret the costly wars she has helped continue. As Charles Fox used to ask in Parliament, why did we fight in the first place for those Bourbons—no friends of ours at any time?"

A bellow of fury issued from the blue coat in front of Betsy. "Damme, sir, how can you utter such sentiments? You know right well Fox lived to sing another tune. He found out what every sensible Briton always knew—except perhaps in this remote spot—the self-crowned French Emperor, this Napoleon Bonaparte is our greatest peril!"

As if sound were color, Betsy saw that name traced in flames across the portrait of the Prince of Wales upon the opposite wall. Stricken with terror, she stumbled across the stranger's buckled slippers and flung herself upon her father.

"Father," she panted, "he isn't true, is he? He isn't a real man like you?"

In astonishment Mr. Balcombe looked down upon his small daughter, conjured, so far as he had been aware of her presence, out of the shadows of the room. So rude an interruption merited reproof. But the doting parent thought only of the child's distress.

"What has frightened you, little one? Who isn't a real man?"

"That Boney! Napoleon Bonaparte. Hasn't he horns on his head and can't he fly through the dark? He isn't real, is he?"

Stroking her hair, Mr. Balcombe said calmly, "Why, Betsy, you must know surely that Napoleon Bonaparte is Emperor of the French people. Yes, he is a man like me—albeit rather more of a genius, I should say. Who has been telling you ghost stories?"

Gripping the buttons on her father's knee-breeches, Betsy still gazed up at him in anguish. "Then, if he's real, will he come here? Will he kill us all?"

Mr. Balcombe took her by the elbow. "No, my pet. This rocky little island would never tempt the great Emperor so far from France. Besides, even if he did come here"—Betsy felt her father shake with laughter as he exchanged a wink with his guest—"he wouldn't hurt a hair of your pretty head. Boney is, I understand, very tender with the fair sex. Now shake hands with our guest like a good child, go to bed, and talk no more nonsense about terrors with horns."

Still a-tremble with the effect of shock, Betsy spun on her toes and gingerly offered her fingers to the tall man. Pressing them gallantly between two large white hands, he said gravely, "Miss Betsy, allow me to say that your fears are not so foolish as your father pretends. I confess I am afraid, too. The Corsican called Bonaparte is a wicked enemy to the peace of Europe. Do your best, I beg of you, to convince your father of the fact."

Up in the nursery again, the little girl flung herself into

[13]

a deep chair and screwed her fists into her eyes. So! He was a human being so powerful that he might even conquer England—this Napoleon! True, her father laughed. But he always laughed at danger—for instance, that time his horse bolted down the mountain.

Across these reflections cut her sister's voice full of grown-up reproach. "Betsy Balcombe, I'm ashamed of your ignorance! You'd better waste less time on French picture books and study history. The very idea of your asking if the French Emperor were a real man! What would he be—a unicorn? Why, he's the most terrible general that ever lived. Father ought to make you read the newspapers from England so that you won't disgrace us all."

For once Betsy had nothing to say. She was too busy somewhere deep down inside her own self, trying to unfasten the image of a horned devil she had put there and to substitute instead that of a man of flesh and blood. Emperor of the French people! Did he wear a crown like the one King George Third wore on Coronation Day? But he couldn't be like him. King George was kind and good, and this man was called "an enemy of peace." Probably he marched before his regiments as Captain Hodson did up at Deadwood on the King's Birthday. Only Napoleon had thousands and millions of soldiers to follow him and, instead of shooting at targets, they shot down people and then took their houses and gardens and rabbits away from them. Father said the Emperor would not come to St. Helena. But suppose he did!

"Miss Betsy, suppah is ready. Why you so quiet, child? You sick?"

"Boney Will Get You!"

The little girl opened her eyes upon black Sarah in a glance of disdain. What an ignorant old thing she was, to be sure, for all her commanding airs. Telling her that a real man, a great king who sat on a throne in an ermine cloak, was a devil with horns! Napoleon must be far more terrible than that to make the big chap downstairs so afraid.

As she took her place opposite Jane, Betsy saw something on the supper table which brought her joyfully back to the present. "Oh, splendid!" she crowed, "we have strawberries tonight!"

But only for the moment did she forget the Man of Destiny.

BETSY LEARNS TO HATE THE ENEMY

After that night Betsy determined to find out about the French Emperor. Stung by her sister's taunts, she announced plans for study which quite terrified Miss Breen, the governess.

"You must teach me French and English history," she commanded, "I want to know everything Jane knows—yes, and everything father knows, too."

Modern history was more to her liking, she found, than any other lesson—even French. Moreover, after a year or so of work, she took more interest in grown-up conversation. For people often mentioned the men she read about, such as Nelson who died a conqueror at Trafalgar; Charles Fox, the great Whig; Viscount Wellington and the powerful Lord Castlereagh. She even began to look over the newspapers and wished they did not arrive four or five months old.

Always she hoped to read of Napoleon's defeat. But the list of his successes grew ever longer. When Betsy learned that his new wife, Marie Louise of Austria, had given him a little son, she knew this dangerous power would be handed down. Already the baby was called "The King of Rome." What puzzled her most was how the United States, way off out of Boney's reach, could choose to be friends with France instead of England. Indeed, she could never understand why the Colonies had ever been so foolish as to break away from England at all.

One day when she was skimming through a newspaper she came across an item which sent her scampering off to find her father. Since he was nowhere in the house, she went through the garden up to the pavilion, a large, vine-covered building perched on a rocky height some distance away. There he was seated at a table, busy over some papers with his business partner, Mr. Fowler from Jamestown.

With curls all on end, Betsy dashed up the path. "Father," she cried, "is it true that those Americans are fighting England again?" She observed that Mr. Fowler, an old-fashioned fellow, who still wore a curled brown wig, was glaring at the intruder. But to the welcoming smile of her father she explained breathlessly, "I've been reading the journals that came yesterday on the *Falcon*. They are full of the American war. Our English cannot possibly be beaten, can they?"

Quite gravely he replied, "Who knows? The Yankees are very superior seamen and gunners, little girl. And their blood is up. We goaded them too far."

"Balcombe!" exploded Mr. Fowler, pushing back his wig until the gray hair underneath came in sight. "Surely you don't sympathize with those bold upstarts!"

"Well, have you not read Lord Holland's speeches before the House of Commons? For months he has protested against the Orders in Council which have wrecked American trade."

Betsy was thrilled to find a lesson coming to life. "I've studied about those with Miss Breen," she exclaimed. "But didn't our Parliament have to pass the Orders on account of the French blockade?"

"Yes, chick. They were our reply to Napoleon's command that Europe cease trading with us. And he gave that command because England was trying to persuade Austria and Russia to side with us against France. So it goes in this cursed thing called war."

"Odds fish, Balcombe!" cried old Fowler, half rising from his seat. "Must we submit to this Bonaparte like meek maids? England alone keeps him from striding the world. As for the damned Yankees, they trade with France, our enemy, but not with us and we should trounce them for it."

Mr. Balcombe's arm uncurled from Betsy's waist and he shook his fist almost in the other man's face. "I'm loyal to the British Navy down to the marrow of my bones. Didn't I risk my life in the Battle of the Nile? But I hate war. Furthermore, any member of the British East India Company is bound to have some heart for the Yankees. England has been impressing their seamen right off their own coast. It's a vexing business to have the best of the crew snatched off for the Admiralty's use. Many a time has that happened on the East India Company's clipper ships and I think it is a foul way to man English frigates."

Elizabeth stared at her father's indignant face. It seemed so strange that he thought England in the wrong.

None of the history books ever gave one the idea that she could be. Mr. Fowler looked very angry also. And it was she who had brought on this disagreement. What if these two should quarrel?

Elizabeth bent her sweetest smile upon her father's partner and said softly, "I am so very sorry, sir, to have disturbed you. But Miss Breen cannot explain things very well and I was so surprised at this news." Turning to her father, she added, dropping her eyes demurely, "I might have waited—only the Bennet boys and Basil Porteous and Rose Legg and some others are coming to play at the Briars this afternoon."

Her long lashes lifted to a surprising change in the social weather. Both men were smiling upon her as if she were presenting them with sugar plums. As her father kissed her cheek, Mr. Fowler said pleasantly, "Enjoy yourself, little lady, but don't let your guests eat all the limequats from the garden!"

Walking slowly through the heat back to the bungalow, Elizabeth pondered the sudden fall of that masculine storm, the flattery of those caressing glances. "It must have been because I am pretty," she decided judicially.

To confirm the surmise, she went straight to the full-length mirror in her bedroom. It showed a slim figure in an ankle-length frock of white cotton sprigged with green leaves. Its wide fichu at the neck set off a piquant little face with saucy nose, big, gray-green eyes and small, full mouth—the whole framed in auburn curls. Bright lips and cheeks contrasted with a creamy skin and white, even teeth. Then and there Betsy decided never to neglect such assets and as a result felt quite grown up.

Even her playmates noticed a change in her manner that day. "Why are you so quiet, Betsy?" asked Basil Porteous. "You aren't ill I hope," said one of the Bennet boys, "I wanted to run races with you." "No, it's too hot for races if she's not well," shouted another boy. "I'll swing her in the swing!" "No you won't," put in Gregory Doveton. "I've ridden all the way over from Sandy Bay just to let her try my pony and she can walk him slowly and not get hot at all."

Betsy smiled at all this commotion. She was used to having the boys fight over her, but now she understood better why they did so. "Hush, all of you!" she cried. "Before we go out to the garden I want to show you something that came from England yesterday."

With that she whisked off to the study and came back with a picture printed on soft paper. The youngsters gathered around to stare at the hideous figure breathing smoke, waving a sword and threatening a helpless and beautiful girl.

"The girl is supposed to be Holland," explained Betsy. "Do you know who the ogre is?"

"It's Boney!" everybody shouted.

"I've seen many of those cartoons," said Gregory Doveton. "They do make it plain what a devil that Bonaparte is. And my father gets pamphlets, too, telling the truth about him. He stops at nothing. He even orders his enemies in Paris to be stabbed in the back."

"Jane and I have read this one—though mother didn't know we did," said Betsy proudly. She held out a paper book entitled *Atrocities of the Corsican Demon,* and it passed from hand to hand. "This tells how Boney buries

[20]

his foes alive and how he gave poison to his own soldiers."

"Oh, he wouldn't be as stupid as that," protested Basil.

"They were sick and wounded, you see," said his hostess, "in one of his Eastern campaigns. They couldn't fight and had to be cared for. So he poisoned them. Oh, I wish somebody would poison him. He's a monster."

Still exchanging horrors about their country's enemy, the children walked out to the paddock to see Betsy's white pony, Tom. One by one they took short gallops on his accommodating back. In the meantime Betsy, dignity forgotten, was racing from cow-shed to barn with Rose Legg and the Bennet boys. When they were too hot for further exertion, she led them to the waterfall to sprawl under the great ferns and sniff up the cooling spray.

"Oh, dear, I shall be sent to England to school next year and shall miss all the fun," sighed the Doveton boy. "I love St. Helena!"

"I don't," said Betsy with a vigorous shake of her curls. "It frightens me too much. I love the Briars. But those bare cliffs all around the island and off the shore—ugh! Why, the other day when Jane and I rode over to Plantation House for tea with the Governor's lady, Tom came within an ace of throwing me down a terrible ravine."

"I almost got hit by one of those big rocks that are always tumbling off the cliff," put in Basil Porteous. "It came right down behind me on the road up to Longwood. You know two farmers were killed that way not long ago."

"Well, but I think it's beautiful on the island," murmured Rose Legg. "The colors of the rocks and the English broome and the little pines and the clouds!"

They all agreed with this, but could not deny Betsy's steady assertion that England was far lovelier and cooler and not at all terrifying. When, however, one of the boys slyly suggested that no English place had such wonderful tropical fruits as those in the Briars' garden, discussion was at an end. Everyone sprang up for a raid on those wonderful fruits. They brought hatsful of guava and oranges and limequats to eat in the shade around the fishpond. The boys vied with one another to pick out the best ones for Betsy and that pleased her until she noticed that Rose and one of the other girls were beginning to pout for lack of attention. So she proposed more games—ring around the rosy and hide and seek.

Nobody accused Betsy of being quiet then. She was swifter and more audacious than any of the others. And how she teased them! At last in a wild burst of spirits, she cried out to Gregory, "You think you can jump so well. See if you can jump over the fishpond!" He went to the edge and measured its width with careful eye. Just as he was shaking his head doubtfully, Betsy rushed up from behind, gave him a terrific push and cried, "Jump across!"

At the splash which followed, she shouted with glee. But she did not laugh long. The water was so deep that Gregory could not keep his feet and the others, leaning over the side, had to hold him up while Basil ran for help. And what a to-do there was then! Everyone knew what had happened. Betsy, who was always loyally protected by her friends from blame for leading them into wild escapades, this time had to confess. Gregory's aunt and Basil's mother, who were playing cards with Mrs.

Balcombe, were horrified. To make matters worse, the heat of the day vanished as it often did in a twinkling, and in the cold mist which had come down the sopping boy began to shiver.

In dry clothes borrowed from Mr. Balcombe's wardrobe, he rode away, declaring in loud tones that it was all his fault for being afraid to jump. Betsy did not hear that defense until later. She was upstairs in her bedroom listening to her father's grave reproaches. They ended in a penalty. She was to remain in her room for three days and was to write out ten pages of correct French for Miss Breen.

She didn't mind that very much. What hurt was that now she couldn't go with her father out to the *Falcon* before she sailed. There was a real punishment! For no other kind of expedition did she love so much. Besides, none of the other children on the island were ever taken out to the ships, and her privilege made her the envy of all. As she sat alone in her room that evening she passed the hours in recalling her first trip taken almost two years ago on her ninth birthday.

That had been an exciting morning. Her father had asked her to ride with him down to Jamestown to select her own gift at Mr. Solomon's general store. On the way a mountain goat, plunging down the steep hillside, had frightened the pony. He bolted and dashed part way down the ravine. Mr. Balcombe had praised her horsemanship that day. "You sat Tom well and were not afraid!" he had said. In town they tied their horses at a picket near the public gardens and arm in arm, started across the brief sea boulevard called the Marino.

Suddenly Mr. Balcombe pointed out a ship just dropping anchor about a quarter of a mile away. "I didn't hear the signal gun," said he. "It's an East Indiaman. I must find out about her."

Hardly a vessel anchored in the bay without her father's being obliged to go on board. For not only had he a private business of purveying edibles to the ships, but was in charge of public sales of merchandise for the East India Company. With Betsy skipping happily at his side, Mr. Balcombe went first to the Company office and then down to the landing steps. There a group of people had gathered to watch the ship's longboat approach. Landing on that shore was a ticklish business. For even in calm weather the ocean in this part of the world had a peculiar, rolling swell and oarsmen had to time their strokes with care in order to bring a boat in safely.

"I find I have to go back in the ship's boat to interview the steward," Mr. Balcombe said to his daughter. "I wish I could leave you at the Castle." He glanced hopefully toward the house of the Governor. Surrounded by a moat and guarded by batteries, this building was connected with the Marino by a drawbridge and served both as the Governor's town residence and as a fort. Shaking his head, the speaker went on, "But the Governor's lady is up at Plantation House. Your mother would not like my leaving you alone anywhere in town. So I suppose I shall have to take you with me."

That was glorious news. It was fun being handed into the heaving boat and exciting to scramble up the swaying ship's ladder. Ordered by her father to remain beside the rail until his return, she watched with interest all that was going on. Sailors were making fast the great white piles of sails, coiling innumerable ropes and mopping up already spotless decks. Orders were shouted. Boats were being lowered to take the officers ashore. Betsy turned around to see one of them scoot over the long, smooth waves. As she did so, the view of St. Helena burst upon her.

She uttered a little cry. How fearful it looked! Now she understood why she had been so frightened long ago when the family landed from England and she had seen the island for the first time. From the very water's edge those cliffs shot up into the sky, dark and threatening. There to the left—that terrible crag which looked like the snout of a giant—how well she remembered it! It had caught her eye the moment she came on deck with her mother. One of the sailors, following her glance, had snatched her up and pointed out the great black mouth yawning against the clouds.

"It will eat you up, baby—snap shut and eat you at a bite! Just as soon as the breakfast gong rings! You wait and see!" Then he had roared with laughter at her scream of terror.

Betsy could almost have screamed again. The massive shape of St. Helena seemed to her more wild and cruel than she would ever have guessed. From the ship's deck it looked like one great mountain floating there on the sea—a mountain carved by some mighty hand. The knife had slipped, Betsy told herself, and by accident gashed those dusky crevices all along the coast. Shuddering, she wondered how she and the others ever had the courage to ride up and down the roads which looked like mere pale ribbons wound across the perpendicular cliffs. Never, except in her childish dreams of "Boney"—which she had recalled again that morning as she always did on her birthday—was anything so awful as this perspective.

Yet the town at the foot of the powerful slopes looked rather sweet. Above the white houses rose the frail spire of St. James' Church and against the towering darkness the lawns of the Castle and the trees in the Public Gardens were marvelously green. She could see the sunshine wink from the bayonet of a sentry and catch the song of fishermen drawing in their nets upon the beach.

Thus her spirits lifted again. When her father came back to show her around the ship, she thought it a great lark. It was even more fun to be landed again on shore in such a great splash of foam that her frock and face were spattered with huge, salty drops. Then and there she determined to go visiting ships as often as her father would take her. And since he liked to indulge her, that proved very often.

Lately, since she had grown so tall, the officers no longer treated her like a child. They offered her a glass of wine with biscuits and talked of the voyage from Plymouth or around the Cape of Good Hope. That was pleasant for a while. But soon Betsy was certain to run off for a game of catch with the cabin boys or a dash into the cook's galley to tease him for a sweet cake. When Mr. Balcombe caught her romping about the deck, he would say sternly, "Lucia Elizabeth, don't be a hoyden! Why can't you try to be a little lady like your sister Jane?"

After the incident of the fishpond, she did try with all

her might. When at last her father took her aboard a ship again, she was very demure. She asked the officers who pressed forward to welcome her, how the war was going. Somehow she could never bear to pronounce the name of Napoleon Bonaparte. But when these men uttered it, she felt a kind of relief—as if their daring lessened the vast shadow he had cast over the world. Not once did she find anyone who had actually seen the Emperor. But tales about him were legion. One description repeated to her by a sailor direct from a wounded soldier lingered in her memory.

The man had said that whoever caught sight of Napoleon on a height overlooking the battlefield felt the day was already lost. That powerful figure in its cocked hat and plain green coat, astride a beautiful Arabian horse, had an air of impregnable strength. He seemed motionless and calm in the midst of the wild turmoil. Once the soldier had glanced up suddenly and there was the Emperor beyond the puffs of gun smoke—not a mere human being, but a resistless will to victory.

What can stop him? That was the question Elizabeth kept asking herself. She confessed to Miss Breen that she was troubled about England. Here was poor King George gone mad and nothing but a Regency to govern. Didn't that have a namby-pamby sound? Often when Mr. Balcombe took her out to a brig just over from England, she would positively dread to hear the news. But at last voices took on a jubilant tone. It seemed that the "Little Corporal," as his soldiers called Napoleon, was meeting with reverses. Reports of terrible losses during the Russian campaign were filtering back through Vienna and Berlin to Paris, and thence to London.

On board the *Marquis of Camden* one spring day a young midshipman held Elizabeth in long discussion of the disaster. She perched on the base of a great gun in the partial shadow of the mizzenmast, looked up from under the brim of her "cottage bonnet" and listened eagerly. Her attention was all the more rapt because the speaker's eyes were so blue and his teeth so white.

"Boney could never catch up with the Russians, you see," said the youthful voice. "They would not give battle, but only drew the French farther on across the steppes. The Czar had no need to risk his Cossacks. He counted on famine and snow to fight his enemies. They say the French soldiers and their horses perished by thousands on that march. I was in Russia once in winter when my ship touched there, and the cold was unbelievable."

"Oh, were you really in Russia?" cried Betsy admiringly. "In my geography it looks ever so far off."

"It is far off," agreed the narrator. "Napoleon was mad to attempt that conquest. He did reach Moscow, guns and all. But that was no victory. The city was burned by the Russians themselves and then the French retreat began. It will ruin the little Corsican, mark my words! He cannot raise another army. He has bled France of men."

Elizabeth was deeply impressed. She talked of nothing else when she returned to the Briars and rushed in to see her mother. Mrs. Balcombe, however, must have thought it rather a jumbled account. For the anguish of freezing French soldiers was jumbled in with the "very nice eyes" of the midshipman and the fun it was to be taken over his trim vessel. As she chattered on, the girl began to think her mother was paying scant attention. She seemed so absorbed in sewing a strip of fur on the wide silk scarf for a new robe. But suddenly the charming face was convulsed with emotion.

"How the mothers of France must hate Bonaparte!" exclaimed Mrs. Balcombe. "He is a monster!"

Betsy had seldom heard her gentle mother speak in so passionate a tone. As she stared at her in silence, she saw rise up again the dreadful, horned image of her infantile dreams. But in a moment the tension eased. Mrs. Balcombe put down her thimble and said in her usual tone:

"Go, bring me your white cambric frock, dear. I must attach a new ribbon to the waist. You must look your prettiest to meet Miss Laura Wilks tomorrow at Plantation House. She has just arrived from Bath, you know, to join her father and her stepmother."

Immediately shadows disappeared in the excitement of anticipation. To people forced to live more than four thousand miles from all they held dearest, nothing was so stirring as to meet a new arrival from the homeland.

And so—what with study and diversion—the brimming days passed swiftly. Long before she had begun to weary of being a little girl, Elizabeth was twelve years old and quite a young lady in appearance. Late in that year of 1814 a momentous day dawned. It brought to St. Helena such news that flags were flown, healths were drunk, sworn enemies embraced one another on the quais, and even stately old Mr. Doveton of Sandy Bay danced something akin to a jig under his plantain trees.

3

GREAT NEWS AND A MYSTERY

There was no warning at all that the day would prove extraordinary. It seemed to Betsy Balcombe only to begin somewhat better than usual—clearer and less hot. She had bounded out of the house early to sniff the fresh air and to say good morning to Tom, the lively pony. As she came back from the long walk to the stables she observed old Toby, the Malay, coming down the grassy avenue from the gateway. The large basket he carried on his head indicated that he had been to the village for supplies.

Betsy ran to meet him. They had been fast friends ever since that long-ago day when she had first arrived from England. Then it was she, a tiny thing, who was transported in Toby's basket up the steep ascent. How gentle he had been with that frightened, uneasy child! "Good morning, Toby! You went early to Jamestown today."

Showing his white teeth in a welcoming grin, the old slave replied, "Mo'nin', Missie. Saw big ship comin' round Sugar Loaf Point. Will drop anchor soon."

Great News and a Mystery

"Oh, Toby, really? How exciting! Perhaps it will bring a letter from grandmother."

Whirling, she pranced back to the house. How she wished her father would take her aboard the ship this morning! At one end of the wide, rose-covered veranda she found little Alexander perched on his hobby-horse and urging it with shouts into a furious gallop. The girl stooped to rumple his curls affectionately. "Bonjour, mon petit!"

"Be careful! Mind my horse! He's running away," cried Alexander indignantly.

His sister laughed. "Bien! That's one thing your goat will never do. I just had a look at him in the pasture and he has grown so fat that I'm sure he can draw your carriage no longer."

"He is not! He can! He took me to town yesterday in my carriage. Mr. Huff could hardly keep up with him."

As she moved away Betsy smiled sardonically. Young as he was, Mr. Huff, the tutor, recently imported from England to instruct the small Balcombe boys, seemed to her only a slightly less poor creature than little old Miss Breen. The son of a schoolmaster, this youth was an odd, sad and fragile person who pored over books the entire time. So it was by no means remarkable that he could be outstripped by even a fat goat.

In the cool hall where mirrors reflected the polished floor Betsy met her father. His hat was already on his head and he seemed in great haste. To her instant question he replied that he was going at once to Jamestown to find out what brig was making port.

"Mayn't I go with you?" she pleaded. "Oh, father, do let me, if you board her."

"No, child, not this time. Well—don't look so melancholy, darling—perhaps you might go. Come down to town by and by—after your lessons. We'll see then. I must be off now. Peter has my horse ready."

It was thus—in a perfectly usual way—that the great day began. No hint of excitement to come. Betsy, however, felt restless and found the schoolroom intolerable. While Miss Breen was out of the room fetching a book, she murmured rebellious criticism in Jane's ear.

"Really, that woman speaks the worst French in the world. Perhaps I still remember how different it sounded when our young Parisian taught us babes in England. I do wish Miss Wilks would consent to give us lessons. Her accent is so very pretty."

"Well," said her sister with an eye on the door, "you certainly speak better than I do, but you might at least try to improve your translations."

Betsy's thoughts, however, were fixed on the great ship riding at anchor outside the town. At the end of an hour she felt she could sit still no longer and with scant explanation or apology flung down her book and pencil and flounced out of the room. To her delight she found her mother downstairs in bonnet and cashmere shawl, ready to walk to Jamestown. Coolly the girl announced that she meant to go along and firmly bore down Mrs. Balcombe's feeble resistance.

It always seemed to Elizabeth that St. Helena's only town had much the shape of a funnel, placed horizontally with its curving cup along the sea. There was but one way to enter the place from the island. For its single street, flanked by residences, boarding houses, shops and a brewery, was wedged between steeply rising cliffs. In contrast the Marino, which met the street at right angles, was built up on one side only and lay open to the sea and a tiny strip of beach.

Less than ten minutes were needed to walk the full length of the main thoroughfare. But hardly were the two Balcombe ladies within the town limits when they became aware of something unusual going on. From a dozen houses men and women were rushing hatless down to the water's edge. There knots of gesticulating people were gathered. As both the girl and her mother quickened their steps the sound of cheering floated back to them. In the distance two soldiers, guns in hand, began to run toward the battery on Sugar Loaf Hill. They saw a group of lads hauling up a huge flag before the Governor's house.

Excitedly Betsy urged on her companion. "Something has happened. Do hurry, mother!"

The girl's heart began to beat very fast. Catching sight of Major Hodson's tall figure, she dropped her hand from her mother's arm and ran up to him. "What is it, Major?" she cried through the din of voices. "What is going on?" Even as she asked the question she saw Mrs. Wilks on the Castle terrace fling her arms about the Colonel with tears streaming down her face.

"News, Miss Balcombe. News!" shouted Major Hodson. "The greatest in the world!" But before he could announce what it was a deafening roar of guns came from the battery above the town. The Major, grinning at the impossibility of making himself heard, snatched off his hat and tossed it in air.

By this time Betsy's curiosity had reached the pitch of desperation. She saw her mother making her swift way through the crowd toward Mrs. Porteous, a Jamestown woman. But, hurrying in the parental trail, the girl almost ran into the arms of Mr. Huff. How in the world did he get down here? He should have been at home teaching the children. She was pushing impatiently past him when the strangeness of his expression rooted her to the spot. In all that throng his was the only face not radiant with joy. Indeed, with tears standing in his eyes, with pale cheeks and tragic mouth, the young man looked as if he had just received a death sentence.

At that instant the salvo of guns ceased. In the hush Mr. Huff's exclamation seemed to ring out like a cry. "Miss Betsy, they've done for him! He's ruined!"

But glad voices were louder. "Three cheers for Wellington!" yelled a lad in Betsy's ear. Someone else screamed, "Victory! Glory be to God!"

The frantic girl, reaching the edge of the crowd, clutched the arm of a young officer from the fort whom she knew and gasped her question once again.

"What's the *news?*" he echoed in a roar. "Why, victory of the Allies! Napoleon's abdicated. The Bourbons have returned again and now there will be peace. Wellington, God bless him, did the trick by pushing the French armies out of Spain. What we've been hoping for came true. The rest closed in on Bonaparte. Paris fell. So now the Corsican will end his cursed life at Elba, a private citizen again!"

[34]

Then Betsy understood. Then she, too, waved her handkerchief and cried with joy and kissed Miss Wilks ex-
uberantly and let James Bennet spin her around in a
triumphant whirligig. At last! At last! The monster was
overthrown. No more war! No more tales of soldiers
dying by thousands upon thousands, of nations enslaved
and fighting for existence. No wonder people were mad
with excitement. C331664 CO. SCHOOLS
The rejoicing kept up the livelong day. Horsemen rode
to the farthest limits of the island with the news. Hearing
it, farmers dropped their hoes, and housewives their
brooms, and everyone set off for town or their neighbors'
to toss down a toast to Wellington, to England, to the
Allies. Governor Wilks gave a dinner to the officers of
the ship which had brought the news, and at the barracks
discipline was relaxed in favor of celebration. Even the
Briars was a center of rejoicing. People dropped in all
afternoon and out at the pavilion a dozen men were always gathered. They gulped down great bumpers of ale
or claret, clapped one another on the back, burst into old
campaign songs and sought by every known means to
express their exultation.

So much a part of all this relief and happiness was
Betsy that she did not remember until she met him in the
hall at twilight the one person who failed to share the
general enthusiasm. But then, seeing a shadowy figure
scurrying out of the study, she sharply recalled Mr. Huff's
face that morning. What had he meant by grief over news
which had gladdened every other heart? Impatiently
she called out the tutor's name.

Mr. Huff was in the act of opening the rear door of

the hall which led into the garden. At the sound of Betsy's voice, his hand dropped from the door knob and he turned sharply. His usually mild voice held a note of defiance as he answered with an abrupt monosyllable, "Yes?"

Betsy looked at him challengingly. "Where have you been all day, Mr. Huff? You haven't been celebrating with the rest of us, have you?"

For an instant the thin, black-clad figure seemed to grow tall and the pale, boyish face blazed. Then the man collapsed into appeal. "Don't mention what you heard me say on the Marino this morning. Please don't. No one would understand. I—I was much upset."

"Why?" questioned Betsy sternly. She felt hostile, yet curious.

With a shrug he seemed to weigh the value of replying. At last he said slowly, "Miss Betsy, I must tell you that unlike most Englishmen, I neither hated nor feared Napoleon. I admired him."

"Oh, how can you?" Betsy had to restrain a savage impulse to slap that grave, defiant face.

Mr. Huff squared his shoulders proudly. "Some day, you, too, will realize that the individual now fallen from his high place was stupendous. He was more than a military genius who could outfight the combined armies of Europe. He was a statesman, also. By his own qualities of leadership he rose to be head of the French people. Napoleon gave them a wonderful code of laws. He taught them to be great. I mourn to think of such genius being snuffed out and all that glorious activity at an end."

Wishing she could stop up her ears, the girl cried,

"Why, he was to blame for the death of thousands and thousands of men. He was the peril of the world. A perfect monster!"

"True. War *does* cost thousands of lives. It *is* monstrous. But this man had a great dream of peace. He wanted a united Europe. Never forget, Miss Betsy, that Napoleon had a spirit vaster than those who fought him down and that now it will take ages to bring about his vision of one European state."

Betsy stared in helpless indignation. In spite of herself his words had aroused in her brain echoes of sympathetic comments read in reviews and occasionally uttered in her hearing. She did not know how to deny them. Yet to admit anything good or admirable about a being whom she had feared and hated since the day she was six years old was impossible.

Suddenly her companion gave her a strange smile. "Miss Betsy, I have only talked so frankly because—well, I don't want you to be afraid to think truly and fairly, even about an enemy." With that he opened the door and was gone.

Even as the latch clicked Betsy heard a footstep behind her and then her mother's voice asking, "What was Mr. Huff saying to you, my dear?"

She hesitated, pulling at the ruffle around her neck with nervous fingers. "Oh, nothing much, mother," she muttered at last.

But her feelings did not match her words. Actually she longed to burst into a tirade against the horrid fellow and wreak some sort of vengeance upon him. For insignificant as he was, he had managed to dispel for her the radiance of this marvelous day. He had planted doubts and questions in the midst of her whole-hearted enthusiasm. She felt cheated. Even months later, when the routine of gaiety and work had obliterated all traces of that thrilling occasion, she cherished a dull resentment against the teacher of her small brothers. The trouble was, she couldn't forget what he had said.

When she read the newspaper accounts of Napoleon's collapse—accounts almost hysterical in the relief they expressed—she found herself doubting whether the Allies would keep the peace. Even certainty that the Emperor had settled down on the island of Elba, powerless and remote, did not give Betsy proper satisfaction. She kept remembering those phrases Mr. Huff had used—"genius snuffed out," "activity at an end." It was preposterous that she should feel any pity for the enemy of mankind. Surely nothing but good could come of the monster's banishment. Faugh! She was disgusted with her own weakness.

Usually she wasn't considered soft-hearted. Jane, who went to many balls and had long ago learned to look up at young men with a blush and a flutter of eyelids, often accused her younger sister of a lack of sentiment.

"You are such a child, Betsy," she exclaimed one evening when Betsy had been impishly teasing her about some admirer. "You only enjoy playing rough and tumble games with boys. When will you learn to prize their admiration and take them seriously?"

The younger girl was perched on the arm of a chair in the bedroom watching her sister at her toilette before the mirror. The candle light gleamed on Jane's white arms and throat and set blue lights dancing in the loops of black hair she was coiling about her ears. Between her fingers sparkling dark eyes shot a mirthful glance toward the armchair.

"Dear me," thought Betsy to herself in surprise, "I believe Jane is pretty, too!" Aloud she remarked, "Well, I don't think anyone here is very romantic. These lads are good for nothing but romps. If only some new people would come to St. Helena! Don't you wonder when you read a biography what it would be like to meet a really great person, a famous person? Just think, Jane, Lord Wellington stopped at this island once on his way back from India. How I wish we had been here then."

Jane, in the act of fastening a pearl brooch among her ruffles, threw back her head and laughed. "Why, you were just an infant. You *are* an odd creature, Betsy. I never knew anyone so much interested in events and in important people—you who once thought Boney was some sort of demon. Pity you weren't one of the boys! You would probably enter Parliament."

At the mention of that hated name Betsy sprang to her feet. "Jane," she asked breathlessly, "can you understand anyone's admiring that—that Emperor?"

The other girl had arisen also for a final complete survey of her costume in the mirror. In a vague tone she answered absently, "Well, father, you know, rather does. He said only yesterday to Colonel Wilks that Bonaparte is the greatest man now living. Oh, pshaw, look at that ruffle. I shall have to call Mathilda to take a stitch in it!"

Before she could move toward the bell rope, however, Betsy seized her wrist. "Father said that?" she exclaimed, eyes wide with amazement. "Why, I didn't know—he never said anything of the kind to me—oh, how could he? Wasn't the Governor shocked?"

"Mercy, how excitable you are! Do let me go—I shall be late for the ball. The Governor didn't look shocked. What difference does it make what anybody thinks now? Boney is safe in Elba and nobody will ever hear of him again. Now please go away and let me finish dressing. Otherwise I shall most certainly be late."

Betsy rushed out of the room, determined to find her father. But when she reached the hall below she heard the sound of men's voices in the dining-room. Then she remembered that Mr. Doveton, who, with his spinster daughter, had dined at the Briars that evening, must still be sitting with his host over their port. Bother! When she was married, she would never give in to that tiresome custom, but would make her husband and the other men leave the table with the ladies.

Out on the veranda, the girl stood watching the moon-lit mist drift through the palm trees like silver smoke. She felt strangely agitated. That her father's opinion should agree with Mr. Huff's was a severe blow. Was it possible that she, also, would have to turn a somersault and learn to admire the hateful tyrant?

At that moment she heard down the grassy driveway the creak of wheels and the sound of gay voices and laughter in treble and bass. It was probably Mrs. Skelton, the Lieutenant Governor's wife, and her party arriving to collect the Balcombes for the ball. For the first time Betsy almost wished she were old enough to join them. They would dance half the night to gay music and eat lovely things for late supper. Perhaps, after all, such an affair would be as lively as a game of Blind Man's Buff.

From the farthest and darkest corner of the veranda, the girl observed the ensuing gay commotion. Two young men sprang off their horses, leaped up the steps and brought down the brass knocker with a great clang. Servants came running to receive the guests, to warn Jane, to announce the visitors to Mr. and Mrs. Balcombe and the Dovetons. From the stable horses were brought around. Immediately the hall was full of people exchanging greetings and collecting hats and shawls. There followed a rush of figures into the moonlight.

After the sound of voices, wheels and hoof-beats had finally receded, Betsy walked slowly into the silent house. No one was visible except Mathilda who was moving softly about the drawing-room to snuff out the candles and straighten the chairs. In the study a reading lamp was burning and the girl strolled in to find a book. There on the table under the light was a copy of the *Quarterly Review* spread open as if someone had just been reading it. A line of scarlet ink had been traced around two paragraphs on facing pages. Betsy leaned over to see.

Here was an article about Napoleon's fall and his present life on the island of Elba. The number was dated October, 1814. It must have just arrived for this was April, 1815, and it took about six months for any review to reach the island. Who had marked that article? Was it Mr. Huff or her father? She looked about her and listened for an instant. But the quiet was unbroken by even a footfall. Sinking down, with her elbows on the table, the girl began to read those ink-framed sentences:

One hears nothing but whispers of his intrigues with Milan, his correspondence with Murat, the number of mysterious visitors whom he receives and the corps of troops which he endeavours to raise.

Be these suspicions well founded or not, it must, we think, be admitted that Elba is one of the most injudicious places of exile that could have been assigned to Bonaparte.

The reader felt a curious prickling of her scalp. Why, this meant—yes, it was horribly clear. The writer believed the Emperor was plotting on his island and might escape. Alarm was in every word. For an instant she felt a return of unreasoning childish terror and might almost have cried out again as once she had, "Will he come here? Will he kill us all?" She wished the house were not so still and empty.

Firmly she told herself that Boney was finished. Without supporters he could never shake his mailed fist at the world again. Surely even admirers such as Mr. Huff and her father didn't want the Emperor back on his throne! Quickly she turned to the beginning of the article. But it was difficult reading. When, some time later, old Sarah came shuffling down to find out why her little Missie was not in bed, she beheld the auburn head dropped upon folded arms beneath the reading lamp. Napoleon's implacable enemy was fast asleep.

Not all next day could Betsy discuss this disturbing news with her father. He was off to Jamestown at an early hour and in the afternoon she went to a party for boys and girls at the Dovetons' lovely place on Sandy Bay.

Great News and a Mystery

Almost as soon as they arrived the guests raced down to the sea. It was marvelous there. The waves had hollowed strange caverns in the rocks and on all sides crags, like vast stalagmites, shot upward in shimmering pyramids of color. The children explored until the girls were breathless with heat and made off by themselves to wade along the beach and giggle happily at nothing.

It wasn't until after the elaborate tea that Betsy recalled her alarm of the night before. Then the sunset gun fired from the battery on the heights of Sandy Bay started that nerve throbbing. Springing up from the divan where she had been watching Basil Porteous make shadow pictures on the wall, she went into the library to find old Mr. Doveton. Probably he had read the *Quarterly* and would tell her what to think.

But Mr. Doveton had not read it. He shook his fine white head contemptuously at the question. "Child, I read no printed stuff and nonsense about Europe. They are always embroiled in wars over there and what the writing folk think about it is no concern of mine. St. Helena, where I was born and raised, is what I care about."

Betsy thought indignantly, "Everyone is always quoting Mr. Doveton. He sits on the St. Helena Council and is important. Yet he doesn't really care whether peace is going to last!"

Just as she was turning away, he said with sudden curiosity, "Why did you ask me about the *Quarterly*? Surely a child like you does not trouble to read it!"

"I do, sir. I was reading about Napoleon Bonaparte at Elba. It is thought he might escape."

"So! Well, well!" The old gentleman took a pinch of snuff. "Perhaps the French want him back. Bonaparte took their men and boys for all his wars, but, after all, he did much for agriculture and they say he set cotton and silk mills to running, too. Oh, he was a tyrant, no doubt. But the frogs will never be loyal to that pigheaded Louis Eighteenth!" Suddenly Mr. Doveton laughed. "My dear, I talk as if you were a man—and of my age. What should be in your curly head except dreams about some comely lad?"

With a furious blush Betsy stamped upon the floor. "I've studied history, sir! I do care what takes place. That is what I came to ask you—whether that monster of a Boney will get loose and bring on another war."

Mr. Doveton's blue eyes twinkled. "Why, you must be a blue-stocking, as the French call ladies who use their heads! Well, go back to your playmates, child, and trouble no more about the Corsican. He's safe at Elba, mark my word, and will never take ship for St. Helena to disturb your happiness." He patted her cheek. "There will always be wars, however, Betsy. Men like to fight. And women—bless 'em—love nothing so well as a fine uniform—except the fine fellow who wears it." Laughing heartily at his own joke, he turned back to his bookshelves.

Seething with a rage she could not understand, Betsy paused on the threshold of the parlor. Voices shrilled her name and bade her join the game of cards started by the others. She neither moved nor answered. She wanted someone to talk to her as if she were grown up, as if it mattered what she thought. Suddenly, with a shock of distaste, she knew who would gratify this wish. It was Mr. Huff.

Why was she so sure since she seldom saw him? As her pony plodded homeward Betsy asked herself this question. The young man spent most of his free time in the loft of the pavilion where he had a room piled to the ceiling with books and papers. Yet she could not down her impulse to seek out this strange individual. A few days later, with the delicate diplomacy of her temperament, she carried it out.

After school hours she lay in wait, a crouching tiger, behind a clump of dwarf palms near the pavilion. When she heard Mr. Huff approaching, she sprang out with such a savage howl that the poor fellow staggered backward, pale and trembling. Glaring at her angrily, he panted, "Why—did—you do that?"

Already she was blushing with contrition. Dolefully she muttered, "I thought it would be fun. I am sorry, Mr. Huff."

"Ah, well"—the tone was bitter—"why should an exile expect even common courtesy?"

Betsy raised an eager face. She never held a grudge against herself very long. "Are you an exile? Like Napoleon Bonaparte? I wanted to ask if you wanted him to escape and return to France."

Mr. Huff looked at her searchingly. Apparently reassured by the candor of her eyes, he answered, "It must have been you who read and crumpled the *Quarterly Review* in which that event was predicted. A cheap and prejudiced piece! Oh, would more Englishmen appreciated this great being! He is like your magnificent waterfall yonder—driven onward inevitably—not to be dammed up!"

"Suppose he got free?" cried Betsy.

The melancholy eyes dilated. "I don't know. Anything might happen." His voice grew excited. "I have read about him day and night. He haunts me. Nothing explains him. I could wish—" He broke off with a shrug.

Betsy said in a cajoling tone, "It is all so puzzling, Mr. Huff. I've found out that father admires Boney, too. But most people hate him as an enemy to liberty. Wouldn't it really be terrible if he came back to the throne?"

Fixed upon her now was exactly the look she had craved, response not to a child, but to another human being. "It is bewildering, Miss Betsy. Because the Emperor abused his power, one hesitates to wish him back. Yet—who is there to match him for genius? I am not glad his day is done. No, I cannot rejoice in that."

The voice had dropped. As if in a dream, Mr. Huff began walking away, but suddenly turned back. "All the same, Miss Betsy, it is good that your soul has opened a crack to what Napoleon really is. Somehow"—he gave her an intent look—"I think that is going to be important."

Betsy remained staring after him. What in the world could he have meant? The words gave her a creepy feeling, as if they were prophetic.

It was, indeed, a prophecy which was spoken that afternoon. Five months later it came true. One rainy October day the clang of the brass knocker rang through the Balcombe house like a signal of fate. Whereupon, there entered, shrouded in mystery, cloaked in authority, a messenger with words of such import that Betsy's whole world reeled as if from an earthquake.

4

ENTER THE EMPEROR

That day convinced Betsy once and for all there was such a thing as luck. Immediately after luncheon an irresistible drowsiness had caused the girl to slip away from the group around the coffee table and shut herself up in the study. There, curled on a divan in a far corner with an Indian afghan pulled up over her, she fell into a deep sleep.

Of course, the knocker's tremendous clatter wakened her with a start. She sat up listening. The sound of a man's voice, the reply of a servant, her father's welcoming tones, footsteps, the sudden turn of the study door knob and Mr. Balcombe's voice saying, "Come in, Captain. Here we can have absolute privacy." Betsy took one wild look about for escape. But there was none. All she could do was to snuggle deep under the rug again, trust to the darkness of the day for protection, and hope that the dialogue would not ruin her pleasant afternoon nap.

At the stranger's first words, however, the listener grew wider awake than ever before in her life. With taut nerves she lay straining not to lose a syllable.

"Mr. Balcombe," said the man, "I bring strange news, too strange to keep long. In a few hours all St. Helena will be in an uproar. We must work quickly before the secret becomes known. I landed but half an hour ago from the *Icarus* and had myself directed instantly to your house. Shortly I hope we may go together to see the Governor."

"And the news, Captain?"

"Be prepared for a surprise, sir. In three days Napoleon Bonaparte will be landed on this island, a prisoner of war."

Even as her heart leaped up in her body Betsy heard her father make a movement as if staggering from a blow.

He gasped out, "In God's name, Captain! What is this?"

"It is the truth."

"But—he was at Elba. How is it possible?"

"You mean to say you've heard nothing? Nothing of his escape, of his seizing the French throne again? What, sir—nothing of Waterloo? It's unbelievable!"

"Waterloo?" echoed Mr. Balcombe in a tone of intense excitement. "What does that mean?"

"The greatest battle, Balcombe, since Carthage fell. Wellington—they've made him a Duke now—defeated Bonaparte in a terrible combat. The Prussians came up at the day's end to finish and the French were routed utterly. Man alive, you've had no word of this great victory? No hint of it at all?" The Captain's low-pitched voice rose almost to a shout.

"None. It takes four months, at least, for journals to

[49]

get here. Go on, Captain, quickly. When was this? What happened then?"

"How can I give you these tremendous facts all in one breath? I never dreamed— Well, after the battle, on June 18, the Corsican fled to Paris. The Allies pursued and finally surrounded the city. Again Napoleon escaped; this time to the sea. He wished to take ship for America. But the British fleet was guarding the coast. Captain Maitland stood outside Rochefort in the *Bellerophon* and to him, at last, on July 15, Boney surrendered."

Betsy slid the cover down from her face. She was choking, trembling. She wanted to scream. Still more, however, she wished to listen and to remain undiscovered. Around the corner of a cushion she could see the two men standing in the middle of the room, the Captain with hat still on his head, and cape sweeping from his shoulders almost to the floor; her father leaning for support upon a chair, his face pale with emotion.

"Who would have guessed—?" he was gasping. "Heavenly powers! Surrendered to the British! You mean—all alone?"

"Almost alone. Friends were with him. Four of them are with him still and will land here, too, sharing his exile."

"Exile! But—of course! They've sent him here for safety. Who made that decision?"

"The ministers. They had to act quickly. Bonaparte protested with all his might; declared that it was not fair, that he had voluntarily asked protection from a favorite foe. He wished to settle down in England. Hah!

Can you conceive of Boney as a country squire?" The
Captain gave vent to a growl of angry laughter.

Betsy saw her father fling out both his hands in a ges-
ture of protest. "Well, but after all, it does seem harsh.
Not much protection in being sent a prisoner to St.
Helena!"

With doubled fists at his waist and elbows pushing
back his cloak, the stranger seemed to strut without moving. "Come, Balcombe, no false sympathy! We've had
enough of that. The fools who admired the fallen tyrant
raised a great howl to madden the government. All the
same, between the day he went aboard the *Bellerophon*
and his final start down the channel in the *Northumberland,* only twenty-five days passed. Quick work, I'd say.
Admiral Sir George Cockburn conducts him here in the
frigate. The *Havanah* and several transports follow along
with the Fifty-third Regiment commanded by Sir George
Bingham. Your population will be almost doubled and
we must be prepared. Only three days, remember!"

"And the Emperor? Is he to be imprisoned?"

Again the watcher saw a vehement flap of elbows make
the cape swirl out. "Not that title, sir! It is forbidden.
'General Bonaparte' now by order of the Prince Regent.
As for the prison, a house will do, properly guarded.
Some freedom is permitted. But what house? That's why
I approached you first. Come now, let's proceed to Colonel
Wilks'. He must be told at once. There is much to do."

Both men moved to the door. Then, with his hand on
the knob, the Captain turned back and murmured, "Balcombe, say nothing of this yet to your wife or family.
Let us avoid confusion as long as possible."

The latch clicked sharply. They were gone.

Instantly Betsy sprang to her feet. But the room reeled around her. She felt ill. Sinking into a chair, she sat unable to move. All her being spent itself in an endless repetition of the phrase, "In three days!" Childish images of dread fled past her and she refused to realize that she might see with her own eyes this figure of frightful legend. How the afternoon passed she never knew. But finally the weight of the secret was lifted. At last the news was told.

In the bedlam that ensued, her own personal shock was eased. Indeed, she now began to enjoy the advantage of her unintentional eavesdropping. Prepared by it, she wasted no time, as did her mother and Jane in asking over and over whether it could be true that Napoleon would be landed on St. Helena. As tongues wagged and questions exploded, as people came rushing up from Jamestown with fresh bits of information, Betsy was able to snatch out of the confusion facts to fill in the outline sketched by the officer from the *Icarus*.

Mrs. Skelton, stopping on her way up to Longwood, regaled the company with a tale. A Lieutenant just arrived on the British ship had described to her how the English coast towns received the news of Napoleon's presence on the *Bellerophon*. "You know," said Mrs. Skelton, "that the vessel went straight from France to Brixham and then to Plymouth. The enthusiasm aroused everywhere by the man Wellington had just defeated was perfectly disgraceful. Everybody in those towns—men and women alike—spent their time in rowboats circling round and round the frigate just to get a look at Boney.

The instant he appeared on deck the entire bay would ring with cheers. Hats would be doffed and kerchiefs waved. Hour after hour this went on. Oh, what folly! Our terrible enemy!"

Betsy could imagine the scene—the bright ribbons on the ladies' hats, the flash of dripping oars, the tense excitement. Would it be like that here at St. Helena?

Now Captain Hodson, over from Meldivia, his place near the Briars, was adding something new. "Worse than that, ma'am, in my opinion," he drawled in his heavy voice, "was Admiral Hotham's softness toward the Corsican. It seems that the flagship, *Superb,* arrived off Rochefort in the Basque Roads the very morning Boney gave himself up to Maitland. So the Admiral had himself rowed at once to the *Bellerophon.* When he met the infamous captive he uncovered, Sir Harry did, and remained bare-headed all the time he was in his presence. Just as if the tyrant were still Emperor."

Pausing for the expected murmur of disapproval from his audience, the Captain went on: "Following that cue Maitland whipped off his hat likewise. Next day Admiral Hotham invites Boney over for breakfast and has the yards of the *Superb* all manned with the pick of his ship and a complement of marines drawn up on the quarterdeck to do him honor. On the *Bellerophon* while he waited to learn his fate, Napoleon had Maitland's cabin the entire three weeks and was served by his own lackeys and courtiers in true imperial style."

Mrs. Balcombe, who had been chatting with Miss Polly Mason at the opposite end of the room, now called out,

"Has anyone heard how many of his suite the Emperor brings here?"

Mrs. Skelton opened her lips to answer. But at that moment Mr. Balcombe entered the room. His coat was wet with the rainy mist. After his hours of riding and discussion, he looked weary and disturbed. Bowing briefly to the company he glanced at his wife.

"I heard your question, my dear, and here is the answer." Reaching into his coat pocket he drew out a paper. "A list as long as your arm. At the bottom are the servants, including a steward named Cipriani. At the top are the faithful four friends—General Gourgaud; Count Las Cases, the Chamberlain and his son; Count and Countess de Montholon and their son; and the Grand Marshal, Bertrand, his wife and two children."

"The famous Bertrand?" echoed Miss Mason eagerly, "the one who was with him in so many campaigns and followed him to Elba?"

"Yes, the same." Mr. Balcombe sank into a chair with a sigh of fatigue. "It's really a marvelous example of devotion. The Emperor could make friends, it seems, as well as enemies."

"But where are they going to put this retinue?" Mrs. Skelton's lips curled scornfully over the question.

Betsy saw her father look fixedly at the speaker for a moment. Then he said, "Well, Madam, there are no secrets now. In fact, I was going to ride over to discuss the matter with you and Mr. Skelton this evening. Subject to the approval of Admiral Cockburn, Governor Wilks thinks perhaps Longwood may be used for Napoleon's— ah—residence."

"Longwood?" Its proprietress sprang to her feet, amazement in her face.

In the brief pause that followed, Betsy remembered something that had happened many years ago. Her first view of that barren plateau and a gray cloud-shadow over it, her frightened outcry and her father's soothing her. Connecting Boney with that place had been mere baby nonsense. Yet here was the vision coming true.

Mr. Balcombe said, "Yes, Mrs. Skelton. I regret your having no summer home, but sacrifices are the rule of the day. We are under orders from now on. St. Helena is to be controlled, not by the East India Company, but by the Crown."

"I wasn't thinking of that, sir. But Longwood—for the Emperor? It is just a farm house. We have never improved it. Our island rats over-run the place and only a few rooms are habitable. It seems—well—I confess I am shocked. Has Colonel Wilks forgotten the Tuileries Palace and the Champs Elysées and Josephine's beautiful Malmaison? Surely the man who lived in such splendor cannot be treated thus. Surely, an unnecessary insult!"

Betsy in her corner clinched her hands together in despair. How could adults change front so swiftly? Did everyone secretly worship Napoleon in spite of spoken derision and hatred?

"They will have to renovate the house, of course," Mr. Balcombe replied. "In the meantime General Bonaparte— that is the official title—will be placed in the Porteous house down at Jamestown. But we can do nothing definite until the *Northumberland* arrives. Lord save us, what a moment that will be!"

It was, indeed, a moment. Betsy, who had risen at dawn the morning of October 15, was with her mother on the Castle terrace when the lookout's gun on Sugar Loaf Hill boomed out its warning signal. Hardly had the echoes died away when the Marino was jammed with people on foot and horseback. To Betsy's astonishment they gathered silently and remained as if under a spell of dread, without talk or laughter. Every eye was fixed on the billowing sails in the distance.

Gradually the dark speck beneath the spreading canvas took shape. Above the uneasy mutter of the crowd one voice sang out, "That's the *Northumberland* for sure. It flies the Admiral's flag on the foretopgallant-mast."

At last, after various tacks in response to the trade winds, the huge frigate with its triple tier of guns swept into the roadstead. At once the pilot's cutter of St. Helena put out from shore. As it did so, a detail of soldiers, guns in hand, took their posts across the Castle moat. Moving back, still in hypnotized quiet, the people remained watching the *Northumberland's* sails drop down.

After a time the cutter could be seen returning to shore with two figures in uniform. It was soon apparent that they must be Admiral Cockburn and Sir George Bingham. At the landing steps several officers met them and they presently came on across the drawbridge to the echo of a respectful huzzah. The brief colloquy which followed ended abruptly when horses were brought up. The two commanders mounted and, accompanied by a volunteer escort, rode swiftly across the Marino and took the road around Ladder Hill which led to Plantation House.

Betsy's eyes came back from their retreating figures to

the ship. Somewhere on board was the man who had made all Europe tremble. Was he out on deck to look at his place of exile? For an instant, remembering her own frightened first impression of St. Helena, the girl felt a small throb of pity. Then she tried to imagine the approaching moment when she might see Napoleon in the flesh. It made her tremble to think of it. Nevertheless, even when word was passed around that none of the passengers would be landed that day, Betsy was reluctant to leave the spot. Well she realized that Jamestown was the scene of a human drama which all the world would like to witness.

Neither that day nor next, however, did its action begin. Mr. Balcombe, giving stern orders that nobody was to leave the Briars, was away from dawn till late afternoon. When he arrived, the entire family was gathered on the lawn to greet him—the ladies with their needlework, the small boys with a game of toy soldiers, played under Mr. Huff's supervision. Springing from the saddle with boyish energy the newcomer exclaimed, "I've been out to the *Northumberland!*"

"What!" An outburst of questions assailed him. But Betsy's shouts were loudest. "Oh, father, did you see him? Does he look like an ogre? When is he coming ashore?"

Laughing and pushing away the small boys clinging to his knees, Mr. Balcombe replied, "Hush! No! Have mercy! The Emperor—or rather, General Bonaparte— was in his cabin and did not come out. He is not to land until tomorrow evening and will go directly to the Porteous house. The transports have arrived, however, and there is a great commotion to get the officers and soldiers billeted."

Later, over a cup of tea, the master of the Briars gave a fuller report of his day. He had had pointed out to him most of Napoleon's official suite. General Gourgaud was a mercurial young man with a long nose and sloping forehead. Madame Bertrand, wife of the Grand Marshal, was very thin and tall, and seemed weighed down by melancholy. Dr. Warden, the ship's surgeon, had said that when she first learned that her husband meant to accompany his chief to St. Helena her frenzy was such that she tried to jump into the sea.

Mr. Balcombe had also met the Irish doctor, Barry O'Meara, whom the Emperor had chosen to be his official physician—"a pleasant fellow, indeed, but with something about him that one could not put one's finger on."

One more interminable day of restlessness! But at last the fateful hour of twilight arrived to find Betsy, clinging to her father's arm, in the front line of the crowd before the public gardens. The girl's strained alertness noted every detail of the scene—the dank, salt smell of the sea wall, the lights twinkling in the nearby houses and far up in the sky where the forts frowned over the sea; then the sound of oars coming over the water and a murmur of talk out there in the dusk. The crowd, massed closely on both sides of the cordon of armed guards from the drawbridge to the Porteous house, stood in hushed expectation as if one single heart of excitement beat for all.

Now this multiple creature stirred and swayed with eagerness. Far beyond its sight the boat was landing with a faint rattle of oarlocks. Presently came a mutter of commands and a shuffle of feet. Lanterns flickered. The soldiers presented arms. A pair of tall officers marched by with military tread. Then—was that he—that figure with tricorn hat framing a face of ghostly paleness?

At that instant someone jostling Betsy knocked her bonnet over her eyes. With elbows pinioned in the press, she heard the air humming with exclamations, a few shrill cries, a shouted name. Jerking herself free the girl saw dim figures mount the steps of the nearby house and the soldiers close in behind. In that moment Napoleon must have passed by beyond her vision. Her heart contracted with disappointment. But all at once she felt very tired, seized the arm nearest her and, finding it belonged to Mr. Huff, was not surprised to feel that it trembled.

Betsy slept ill that night and awakened late. By the time she had finished her morning chocolate she found her father walking up and down the lawn in earnest conversation with Mr. Porteous from Jamestown. When he had gone she ran out, tucked her hand in her father's arm and walked beside him with such mighty steps to match his that her skirt fell back to show the long, lace-trimmed pantalettes beneath.

"Tell me," she begged, "what has happened since last night?"

Mr. Balcombe seemed ready for confidences. "I have just learned that the Em—er—General Bonaparte dislikes his abode. Half the night he was disturbed by people struggling with the sentries to get a peek at him through the shutters. He wishes to be moved from Jamestown. I am to consult Colonel Wilks. But at present he, together with the Admiral and Sir George Bingham, is escorting

Napoleon up to show him Longwood, his future residence. Good heavens! I can still hardly believe all this is
fact."

"Shall I ever see him? Will he meet people?" asked
Betsy.

Her father made no reply. He had halted and his eyes
had fixed upon a distant point. Following his glance, she
uttered a cry. Plain to be seen across Ruperts Valley in the
bright sunshine was a defile of horsemen climbing the
steep road. Four of them, going toward Longwood! It
was undoubtedly the Governor's party of investigation
and one of those tiny figures was Napoleon. Until a curve
of the road hid them from view the girl stood without
moving a muscle.

Then with a whoop she dashed toward the house.
"Frank! Alex! Come, watch! You can see the Emperor
riding up to Longwood."

An hour after luncheon the four figures could again
be descried starting back again. This time the entire
household was gathered at an observation point.

Suddenly Mr. Balcombe said, "Look, they've halted!"
After a pause he added in amazement, "They're changing
their course. They're taking the path in this direction.
Could they be coming here, in the name of Heaven?"

Deliberately the horsemen picked their way down the
steep descent into the ravine. There they disappeared. But
the watchers knew that the only way out of the perilous
place led straight to the Briars' gate. Betsy drifted back
toward the bungalow. Her father was shouting orders.
Her mother ran with Jane into the house. The girl could
hear scurrying feet and Miss Breen's scared treble, calling

to the little boys. She herself remained outside, leaning against a pillar of the veranda, aware, with the blood hammering in her ears, that one of the great moments of her life was upon her.

It seemed a long time that she stood there. Her father came out of the house and without even noticing her began to walk down the long driveway. Suddenly he stopped and threw out both hands. Far beyond at the open gateway two horsemen had appeared, and behind them, two. Then one drew rein and fell back to form a rear guard of three for the advancing single figure.

The great black horse curved its neck proudly and stepped a prancing measure. Astride its saddle of crimson velvet embroidered in gold were a pair of shining black boots and white breeches, topped by a green coat, all a-glitter with medals. Betsy lifted her eyes. The cocked hat! The grave, pale face of classic feature, glimpsed in last night's shadows! Was this the demon so long hated?

Superbly he rode, one with his beautiful horse. The calm eyes were fixed on infinite distance. Through the arch of trees sunlight flooded him with glory. Thus time seemed to recede, leaving isolated and supreme the mighty Emperor. For this was majesty!

Voices now! Governor Wilks was flinging himself out of the saddle. Names were pronounced and bows exchanged. Admiral Cockburn. Colonel Bingham. The towering horseman in the cocked hat bent his head to William Balcombe. Bereft of sense, the paralyzed girl on the veranda yet heard all. The party had lunched at Longwood with the Skeltons. On the way back General Bonaparte had caught a glimpse of the Briars, had liked it, and inquired if he might see it, find out if perchance he might stay there instead of in the town. The Governor had remembered a large pavilion on the place. In short, here they were, dismounting to discuss the matter.

Borne on the wings of terror Betsy rushed into the study. Cowering there she tried to face the inevitable. For, certainly, he would stay if he so willed. Then a new world would begin, stranger than wildest fancy.

Presently she heard her name called. Flushed but quiet, Mrs. Balcombe stood in the doorway. "Come, my dear, you must be presented. Now! Never mind your hair."

So there she was in the Presence. The seated figure made a throne of the rustic chair, an audience chamber of the lawn. Rising from her deepest curtsey, made with trembling knees, Betsy received a smile from finely curved lips, parting to show beautiful, even teeth. A small shapely hand waved her to a nearby chair. As she sank into it and glanced swiftly about, her breath stopped. For she realized that everyone had somehow disappeared and left her alone with Napoleon.

"Vous parlez français, mademoiselle?"

The tone was metallic, the accent blurred. With a mighty effort the girl looked into the gray eyes and answered, "Oui, monsieur l'Empereur, monsieur le Général."

With a pleased expression Betsy's august companion began to pelt her with questions, one after another, as rapidly as her breathless answers were uttered. Who had taught her French? How much history had she studied? Did she find geography to her taste? Could she name the capital of France? "Bon." Of Italy? "Bon." Of Russia?

To the last question Betsy, with mounting assurance, replied, "It is St. Petersburg now, sir, but was Moscow formerly."

At this the green coat bent forward. Piercing eyes bored into hers and a voice of immeasurable sternness asked, "Who burned Moscow?"

Before her now was the terrible man she had dreaded all her life, the merciless tyrant. She felt as if someone had rubbed ice along her cheeks. What could she answer? Well, she knew that any allusion to that disastrous campaign in Russia might offend. Again the question rang out harshly. In desperation she stammered, "Je ne sais pas, monsieur."

In a twinkling the heavens shifted. Napoleon was laughing. It was a hearty, human sound. For the first time Betsy realized that he was plump and short, with a full chin above the gleaming orders on his breast.

"Mais oui, oui, mon enfant!" he said gleefully. "You know quite well that it was I who caused the Russian city to be burned."

With laughter in her ears, she was beginning to feel more like herself. This was a man, not a monster. Impulsively she said, "I believe, sir, that the Russians burned Moscow to rid themselves of the French invaders."

Again he laughed. "You are right, child. That was how it happened. I see you have studied your history of today. We shall have many talks about my campaigns."

Reprieve came for Betsy then. For the three officials had returned from the tour of inspection to discuss it with the personage so incredibly seated on the lawn. Retiring with what grace she could command, the girl hurried off to find her mother. That lady was already in the pavilion giving directions to the assembled servants. Mr. Balcombe was gathering up papers from the table and directed Betsy to help him. The impossible had happened! Napoleon was to live there for a month.

All afternoon the Briars was the scene of wild activity. A clatter of cleansing echoed from the pavilion. Down the driveway galloping officers came and went. They were succeeded by a long parade of French servants and British soldiers carrying pieces of luggage. One grizzled fellow led a donkey which bore strapped to its back the great commander's camp bed which he had used at Austerlitz. Busy as she was, Betsy did not miss these details, nor fail to steal frequent glimpses of the man for whom all this to-do went on. Napoleon was strolling about the lawns all alone. He would look up at the trees and stoop to the roses with an air of complete unconcern. If an officer dashed up to ask a question, he was answered and dismissed with a brief gesture.

Toward sunset the girl encountered in the hallway young Mr. Huff. He was staggering in with a pile of books which he set down on the study floor. Obviously the cyclone had driven him out of his quarters.

"Where are you going to stay?" she asked curiously. "Who is to occupy your room?"

Breathing heavily from fatigue he answered, "The Count Las Cases and his son have my apartment. Marchand, the valet, will have the other garret chamber. Your father has arranged for me to go to the house of the Bennet family for a while. My books will be sent for tomorrow."

"Do you mind? How do you feel about these great changes?" she asked.

A feverish glow came into the tired, boyish face. "Mind? I would sleep on the ground to accommodate the Emperor. It is all too glorious to be believed. Who could imagine—he is so calm, so gentle—that his was the mightiest fall in all history?"

That evening Betsy wished the tutor had been present. His excitement would have been something to see. For, after a dinner brought up to the pavilion from the Porteous house, Napoleon sent over word that he would accept Mrs. Balcombe's invitation to spend an hour with the family. Weariness was instantly forgotten in the intense interest of such a visit.

The guest was magnificently announced by one of the French lackeys. But from that moment on informality was complete. It might have been any pleasant social occasion. With this difference to Betsy! Her fluency in French gave her the most intoxicating importance. Through her were transmitted the visitor's gracious compliments on the charm of the bungalow and the garden. Through her came parental acknowledgments. Indeed, in the realization that her own accent was better than that of the man who had ruled France, the girl's assurance mounted sky high.

Suddenly imperial courtesy warmed with interest. "I see you have a pianoforte. Nothing is more charming than to hear someone play and sing. It is a pity you are too young, mademoiselle."

Always that tiresome remark! Stung by it, Betsy retorted, "But, monsieur, I do play and sing."

As the words left her lips she could have bitten her tongue. Now she was in for it. Nothing would do, she was told, but to make good her boast. Tremulously she went to the piano and, quickly selecting the shortest song she knew, struck a chord. At the end, however, the singer so heartily agreed with the audience about the success of the performance that she sailed confidently into *Ye Banks and Braes of Bonnie Dune.*

"Bon! Charmant, mon enfant! It is the prettiest English air I have ever heard."

Flushed with triumph Betsy spun around on the piano bench. "Mais, non, monsieur, it is not an English air. It is Scotch."

Delighted eyes met hers. "Bien! No wonder I liked it. The English have the most villainous music in the world. Do you know the French song, *Vive Henri Quatre?* Sing that."

"I do not know it, sir."

Instantly the green-coated figure sprang up. "It goes like this." A thoroughly unmusical voice filled the air with a peculiar humming. To the rhythm of the beat, black buckled slippers and white stockings went marching across the room. Bringing up at the piano the enthusiast said, "Now, my little one, what do you think of that?"

Betsy looked up into twinkling eyes. A merry smile bent down upon her. Amazing was the message thus conveyed from the great Napoleon. Plainly, as if put into words, she heard the plea, "Come, cheer me up! Don't be respectful and distant. I need sunshine in this lonely place. I want a playmate to like me for myself. Let us have an amusing time together."

[66]

5

NAPOLEON MAKES A NEW FRIEND

The new life which Betsy had foreseen was in full swing by the third day after Napoleon's arrival. At high noon the girl hurried out of the schoolroom, glad to escape from lessons which, in contrast to all the excitement outside, seemed more intolerable than ever.

As she stepped out on the veranda she heard the plushy thud of hoofs on the turf, the clink of bridle trappings, and the guttural of male voices speaking French. Past the house a group of horsemen were trotting toward the pavilion. She just had time to catch a flashing smile from one of them as he raised a hand to his cocked hat in military salute.

She plumped down on the step to savor the thrill of it. That was the Commander of all the French armies, greeting *her*—Betsy Balcombe, aged thirteen and a half! Wasn't it just too astonishing? He must have been out for a ride with Admiral Cockburn and Captain Poppleton of the Fifty-third Regiment. The fourth member of the party she had recognized as young General Gourgaud who came up from Jamestown to see his chief almost every day. If they returned to town without staying for lunch, she would run up to the pavilion for a moment.

Hardly had she framed this idea when the escort of three rode around the house again and off down the driveway. The next moment Betsy was halfway up the path. Napoleon was chatting soberly with the Chamberlain, Las Cases, and in front of them, staring with thirsty curiosity, stood her little brother Frank. Betsy could have boxed the child's impertinent ears, but she observed Napoleon pat the boy's rosy cheek with absent-minded kindliness. Then he caught sight of her and his face lighted up.

"Bonjour, Mees Betsee!" That was the gay greeting she received every day.

As she drew closer, however, a flick of mischief touched the friendly gray eyes. "You arrive to see le petit Las Cases, I suppose?" She shook her head indignantly. He knew perfectly well that the Count's fourteen-year-old son seemed a mere infant to a young lady acquainted with officers twice his age. But the teasing voice went on. "Alas, mademoiselle, my little page, Emanuel, is too busy even to kiss your hand. And you? Have you been a good child? Have you learned your lessons this morning?"

She stamped her foot with rage. It was too unbearable to be addressed as a babe in the nursery. Flouncing around, she bent down her furious face while pretending to adjust the ribbon at her waist. This show of temper was greeted by a chuckle of satisfacion and a hand shot out to give her ear a hearty tweak.

"Come, Betsee, turn around and let me see your eyes

[68]

so charming with their green light. You have on a new frock. It is prettier than the one you wore yesterday. I do not like frocks to be too short. Then the pantaloons appear and that is not graceful. Yes, you look very seductive. What a pity General Gourgaud did not remain for lunch. He is susceptible. He would pay you compliments."

Entirely restored to good humor by this flattery, Betsy chatted with her companion as they strolled in the small rose garden. She was just describing her study of St. Helena history when her name was called by a servant. He was summoning her to receive Miss Rose Legg who had come with her mother to call. Regretfully she followed him down to the bungalow.

Rose was waiting on the veranda to rush upon her. "Oh, my dear Betsy! What terrible changes have come over the Briars! When I found two sentries at your gate I thought I should faint. They actually refused to let us pass until our names were sent in. How can you bear to have your place surrounded with soldiers all the time? It's just like a military camp."

Betsy had heard her mother mildly complaining about the new régime. Always to be getting passes for the servants and the family to go in and out of their own place was most inconvenient. But she herself hadn't felt the restrictions. Since the center of interest was at the Briars, who cared to leave it? This was not what she said, however. For a wicked idea had suddenly sprung into her head.

Looking gravely into her friend's concerned face, she

replied, "Yes, indeed, Rose, you cannot imagine what it is like here now."

"Oh, Betsy, I've been too much troubled about you to sleep. How frightened you must be to have this monstrous enemy on your very own place!"

This speech offered just the right opening for Betsy's plot. Raising her eyes to heaven, she exclaimed, "Oh, I've been half dead with fright. As a friend you ought to see what goes on. Come with me now—this moment—and look at Boney. Judge for yourself if I'm not to be pitied."

The little heart-shaped face paled with apprehension. The plump figure in pink mousseline drew back. Nevertheless, her own curiosity and Betsy's insistent hand drew Rose up the path to the pavilion and she waited with round eyes while her hostess went to reconnoiter.

Choking with laughter Betsy skipped into the arbor where Napoleon and Count Las Cases were sitting. "Monsieur le Général," she whispered, her eyes dancing, "a little friend of mine is out there near the hedge. She has great fear at the thought of seeing you."

Instantly Napoleon sprang to his feet. Without a word he strode past her, snatching off his hat with one hand and brushing up his hair with the other. Betsy rushed after him. She saw him making for the cowering Rose, his face twisted into horrible grimaces. Suddenly he lunged forward with a savage howl. It was echoed in the shriek of horror uttered by the fleeing damsel. Like a doe pursued by hunters the girlish figure bounded down the path and disappeared around a corner of the veranda.

"You ought to be ashamed, Miss Balcombe."

Glancing around Betsy found Las Cases standing on

[70]

the path above her. His exclamation had been in English and in a flash the girl remembered that the Count had lived in England for some time. The man's thin frame was stiff with disgust. His eyes flashed with the outrage of having his Emperor transformed into a naughty boy. But the girl's companion in crime was shaking with silent laughter.

All at once, repeating his imitation of an ogre, he started toward Betsy. But she nimbly dodged the on-slaught and leaned laughing against a palm tree.

Napoleon smoothed down his hair. "Eh, bien, you have no fear of such a terrible beast? Diable! Go see to your little friend. Perhaps she has fainted. Our scene was a great success, n'est-ce pas?" He exchanged with her a look of triumph. Then his dimpled forefinger pointed to the witness behind them. "Voici Las Cases!" he chuckled. "We have offended the Chamberlain. Grâce à dieu Gour-gaud was not here. He would never forgive us. But good Las Cases will forgive, is it not so?"

Bestowing a pat of careless confidence on the shoulder of the small man, Napoleon waved his other hand at Betsy and mounted the steps of the pavilion.

When the girl returned to the bungalow she found that Rose and Mrs. Legg had departed. "The foolish child was in hysterics," said Mrs. Balcombe. "It seems strange now that the mere sight of General Bonaparte could produce such terror. But since we have all been taught to regard him as a monster, it is not fair to blame Rose."

Betsy listened with the guilty feeling that if her mother knew the trick played on the visitor she would blame someone else very severely. Yet it was difficult to accuse

[71]

herself of misbehavior in the presence of Napoleon. For
he positively encouraged it. A joyous gleam leaped into
his eyes whenever she said anything wild or indulged a
mad caprice. Why? That very afternoon she tried to explain this.

She and Jane were helping their mother serve tea to a
group of official guests. When at last she herself secured
some refreshments she sat down to enjoy it beside Dr.
Warden, the surgeon of the *Northumberland*. At once
they began to speak of Napoleon. The doctor described
how calm and good-tempered he had been on the long
voyage, how readily he had discussed in the frankest possible manner many chapters of his amazing career.

"Don't you think," asked Betsy eagerly, "that perhaps he
was tired of being an emperor? He seems so happy here.
Always so full of fun! He acts—well, just as I feel when
lessons are over."

Upon this she received a long look from her companion. "No," he said slowly, "I cannot think such a man
would willingly have given up absolute power. And his
stupendous energy! He could work eighteen hours at a
stretch—whether it was planning battles or drawing up
state papers. How is he going to occupy himself now?"

Betsy's answer was prompt. "Why, he seems busy all
the time. For one thing he is dictating a history of France
under his rule. Count Las Cases is taking it down. Early
this morning when I reached the garden I saw them at
it. Boney was walking back and forth with his hands
clasped behind him, and I heard his voice talking and
talking without a pause."

"That book will be something to read one day," mused

the doctor. Then as he rose to take leave, he added with a significant air, "But as for his being happy here, Miss Balcombe, Governor Wilks or Admiral Cockburn would, I think, tell you that their famous charge says otherwise."

Next day at a very odd moment Betsy recalled this disturbing remark. Several times Napoleon had told her that the little gate to the arbor and rose garden, which was kept locked against intruders, would always be opened to her. That afternoon, having a reason to avail herself of the privilege, she knocked at the entrance. Then seeing in the depths of the arbor a figure stretched prone upon a cushioned bench, she began to rattle the latch impatiently.

At this General Gourgaud, who had evidently been up for luncheon, came running down the pavilion steps. "Non, non, non," he growled. "Pray do not disturb the Emperor, mademoiselle, he is asleep."

How possessive they were, these French, thought the girl. The young officer was shocked as if she were standing on consecrated ground. Moved by a sharp twinge of jealousy Betsy shook the latch with all her might and called out loudly, "Monsieur le Général! Please open the gate."

"Stop it!" cried Gourgaud angrily and roughly seized her arm.

But, as she shook off his hand and called out again, the figure in the shadows stirred and sat upright. "Qui est là?"

"I am here, monsieur," she sang out. "Betsy Balcombe. I want to see you. But General Gourgaud wishes me to go away. He has hurt my arm."

A deep chuckle floated out from the dusky coolness. "Tell me why you wish to enter, Mees Betsee, and perhaps I shall open for you."

"Visitors are at our house, monsieur le Général. Miss Polly Mason whose place is near Longwood and her niece —a very pretty girl—but really pretty. They long to be introduced."

"Non. I have no wish to frighten any more young ladies, my dear. Please present my excuses."

Hearing this, General Gourgaud uttered a grunt of satisfaction. But Betsy's busy fingers, prying between the pickets, had suddenly found the inside lock and turned the key. In a twinkling the gate flew open. Before her companion could stop her she had danced into the arbor. In the impetuous mood possessing her, she swooped upon a pile of papers lying on the table.

"Now, monsieur!" she cried, waving them in air. "Because you had the bad intention of locking me out I shall keep these papers and discover all your secrets."

From the other side of the table Napoleon called out sternly, "Put them down instantly, little bad one."

But Betsy saw that he was trying not to laugh. Moreover, a glimpse of Gourgaud striding toward her with face of thunder inspired her to further antics. Flourishing the documents over her head, she pranced to the other end of the arbor. "I shall find out everything. Perhaps you have written complaints to Governor Wilks."

Instantly she observed a startled look pass between the two men and she thought of what Dr. Warden had said. Apparently her shot had gone home. It gave her a strange uneasiness. What was there to complain about? Had

Napoleon been telling her mother polite fibs about his admiration of the garden and its wonderful fruits? Didn't he really like the Balcombe family as much as he appeared to? Surely he enjoyed horseback riding and his walks—to say nothing of the fun he and she had together.

In a persuasive tone Napoleon called out:

"Eh bien, Betsee, if you persist in keeping my papers we shall be friends no longer. I warn you."

Her mood had already sobered. Instantly moved by this threat, she laid the loose packet on the table. Then seizing Napoleon's hand in both hers she looked into his face. "Monsieur le Général, I beg you to come down with me to the house for a moment. I shall be so proud. You will make our guests happy. And you will enjoy seeing Miss Carpenter, I assure you."

"Is she as lovely as Mademoiselle Laura Wilks?" asked Napoleon with a sly look at the disapproving face of the other man. "Baron Gourgaud here describes that young lady as exquisite. Already he has fallen in love with her."

"Really?" Betsy impulsively held out her hand to the young man. As he took it she observed that her sudden transformation from bad child to gracious young lady made him open wide eyes. "My felicitations, General Gourgaud, upon your taste. Miss Wilks is the most adorable woman in St. Helena." Then turning again to Napoleon, she repeated her plea. This time he remonstrated no further, but walked with her hand in hand down to the bungalow.

A happy half hour followed. In regal fashion Napoleon dispensed compliments and Betsy proudly observed that the ladies were charmed. Just as they were leaving, how-

ever, a crack appeared in the smooth surface of talk and
again the startled girl beheld dark undercurrents of dis-
cord.

Miss Polly Mason had said innocently in her halting
French, "Perhaps, sir, you will ride up to my place some
afternoon and see my rose garden. It is very pretty."

"Merci, madame." The brief words were spoken with
an accent of irony and a shadow settled on the handsome
brow.

Miss Mason did not notice the change. "Would you be
willing to name a day then, sir?"

"Non, madame. Your governor may not permit so long
a ride. And in any case you would not expect me to pay
a social call under guard."

Betsy's heart squeezed together. She was always forgetting the ugly fact that he was a prisoner.

"I'm sure—" began Miss Mason, but faltered in dismay.
Then the horrid moment was swallowed up in the arrival
of a groom leading the horses. Since Napoleon himself
gallantly lifted little Miss Carpenter into the saddle, the
farewell was pleasant enough. But immediately afterwards Napoleon, with a brief bow to the three Balcombe
ladies, started back to the bungalow.

As her eyes left his retreating figure, Betsy saw Mr.
Huff swing down the driveway. He hurried up to the
trio on the lawn with an air of great agitation.

"Mrs. Balcombe," said he, "have you heard the rules
proclaimed by Governor Wilks? Nobody allowed abroad
after nine o'clock without the parole of the night. At sun-
down the drawbridge is raised cutting off the town from
the beach. No ship of any other nation will be allowed

to communicate with St. Helena. In short, we are all treated more or less like prisoners. There is a fine logic in that, is there not?" He threw back his head and laughed strangely.

Mrs. Balcombe looked at the young man with gentle reproof. "Why, of course, I knew the Governor had made that proclamation. One must accept it as necessary. The presence of General Bonaparte is a great responsibility."

Huff asked fiercely, "Then why did the British government undertake it without preparation? Count Bertrand is furious about the Emperor's accommodations here. With only one room to live in he has to go out-of-doors while the servant makes up his bed. He has no proper bath. All the French say it is outrageous."

Glancing at her mother's troubled face, Jane replied with some heat, "Well, what could we do? Boney himself wanted to stay here. Do the French officers think we should have moved out of the house for his convenience?"

The emotional boyish face took on a look of hurt. "Certainly not, Miss Jane. I heard Madame Bertrand with my own ears speak with gratitude of all you had done up here for the Emperor. But many people believe that Plantation House should have been turned over to the French. After all, the Governor could live in the Castle. But what do the British ministers care—except to humiliate the foe they fear?"

"Dangerous words, Huff!"

Behind them stood William Balcombe. Everyone in that group on the lawn had been too absorbed to notice his approach. The stern voice matched his face and Betsy for the first time in her life saw him as a British official.

His tone had caused the excitable tutor to shrink together as if he were a small lad before an irate head master.

"It is going to be far from easy to keep neutral in this situation," went on Mr. Balcombe, still with his air of authority. "Already the island is dividing into camps and Jamestown seethes with talk. But I assure you the overwhelming majority is for the Governor and Admiral Cockburn and for strict measures in the treatment of General Bonaparte. That, I may add, is the safe side to choose. If you think official procedure is unfair, Huff, keep your opinion to yourself. You can do nothing. So you'd best neither gossip nor listen to gossip. Troublemakers abound."

With this the speaker tucked his wife's hand into the crook of his arm and drew her slowly toward the house. Jane trailed along behind. Betsy, however, sank down upon a rustic seat encircling an old palm tree to weigh these revelations. They made her realize forlornly that the happy-hearted gaiety she enjoyed with Napoleon was merely a childish dream. Looking up she met the eyes of the tutor and was shocked by the wild light in them. Of what could the strange fellow be thinking? For fear he would tell her, she got hastily to her feet and walked away.

During the next few days, however, Betsy forgot everything but the interest of the moment. Every noon, by invitation, she went straight from the schoolroom to the pavilion to present for criticism a page of translation from English into French. If it was good, she was given a pat on the cheek and a sugar plum made by Piron, the French pastry cook.

[78]

Napoleon Makes a New Friend

When he heard of this footnote to learning, baby Alexander decided to join the class. And from one of these occasions Betsy brought away a long-remembered picture. It was of Napoleon sitting on a rough-hewn bench of hemlock under a banyan tree. On the imperial knee sat little Alex playing with the big silver buttons on the green army coat against which he leaned. In the imperial hand was a page of French exercises written in a childish scrawl. Often in later years when she heard Napoleon abused for bloodthirsty wars or for love of imperial pomp, she would recall that peaceful domestic scene. She would hear again the gaiety in his slightly harsh voice as he looked up from the page saying, 'Bon, mon enfant. You show the beginnings of wisdom. Voilà! In that box on the table you will find a bon-bon."

It was a beautiful hand-painted box with a great gold crest on top. As she opened it Alexander scrambled down from his perch and came to look with greedy eyes. "Wait a moment," he said. "I want to fill my own tiny box. It is in my goat carriage out there where I left Billy grazing."

Only two sugar-plums, however, would go in the tiny box. When he had eaten these the small boy looked around for more. But in the meantime Piron had come out to whisk the big box away and Napoleon, suddenly absorbed in reading some manuscript handed him by Las Cases, had walked to the other end of the arbor. Even Betsy had forgotten her brother. On the back of her exercise she was making a sketch. It represented a tall young officer with striking features and proud bearing. She drew this sketch every day. For once during the changing of the guard at the Briars' gate she had caught a glimpse of the original and thought him the handsomest youth she had ever seen. No one, however, seemed able to tell her who he was.

Alexander's next move was quite unobserved. His search had disclosed a little box filled with wee brown balls—undoubtedly some sort of candy, he thought. As many of these as he could he packed into his bonbonière. Then running up to Napoleon he proudly offered him a sample.

Las Cases frowned at the interruption, but his chief looked up from his papers long enough to smile and accept several of the proffered sweetmeats. A second later Napoleon was spluttering, "Diable! Ah—ah—c'est horrible-ça." Betsy jumped to her feet in consternation. The fit of coughing which followed was so prolonged that the Chamberlain fled to the pavilion. Cipriani and another servant came with water. Amidst an indescribable chattering, gesticulating and commotion the chokes gradually subsided to a gasp.

Las Cases turned upon the small boy. "Where did you get those vile pills?" he roared. The frightened youngster stared a moment in surprise and obediently pointed out the little box. In horror the Grand Chamberlain seized him by the wrist. You have given the Emperor a dose of strong medicine. Come with me. I shall report this to your father. It is too much." Off he went so fast that Alexander's fat little legs in their white stockings seemed to twinkle in the sunlight.

As soon as he could speak Napoleon said to Betsy, who was regarding him fearfully, "Never mind. It's nothing. A bad joke—hein? I understand. My son, the little King of Rome, might have done the same. Come, I will show you there are no hard feelings, despite Las Cases. I invite you and your sister Jeanne for dinner tomorrow night." He smiled. "Cipriani's confections will not make you cough, I assure you."

Never was boast more justified. But everything about that occasion was to the last degree fascinating. Not since the French occupation had the two girls crossed the threshold of the pavilion and they looked around the changed place with great curiosity.

In one corner stood the celebrated camp bed hung with green silk curtains. Beside it was a stand which held a large wash bowl and pitcher of magnificent silver. These regal trophies, contrasted with the homely simplicity of the huddled room, shouted of past glory. So did the obsequious manner of Las Cases and his son who behaved as if at a court levee. Betsy, shy and overawed, could not respond to the encouraging twinkle in the eyes of her host. Nor was she put more at her case by the majestic formality with which Marchand, the valet, announced dinner.

The table was set in a big tent pitched behind the pavilion and reached by a passageway enclosed in canvas. In another tent Cipriani and his assistants had rigged up a kitchen. But there was nothing makeshift about the repast. Never could Betsy have imagined anything so splendid as the table service marked with a wreath-encircled "N." After the soup two lackeys filled the wine glasses and passed the simple viands—fish, meat and a few vegetables. Speed and silence characterized the meal, for Napoleon ate swiftly and not very much.

Between courses there was a bit of conversation. "To-day," said he, "I watched from the garden a long defile of British soldiers carrying lumber up to Longwood. Work on the house must be well along already. It was hot for such toil."

"But, sire," replied Las Cases, "that is less than what your soldiers did in Egypt. And nothing compared with dragging cannon and guns through the snow over the Alps in your first Italian campaign. How magnificent that was! I shall be glad when you come to that part of your memoirs."

When the desert appeared Betsy, who had hardly opened her lips, cried out irrepressibly, "Oh, how beautiful!"

Beaming with pride, a lackey had just set in the center of the table a marvelous structure of spun sugar. It looked like a miniature castle with white turrets and a moat of green pistache. To go with it a marron cream was served on exquisite porcelain plates with two gold spoons for each. Betsy had to watch out of the corner of her eye to discover that one of the spoons was for coffee, poured into fragile Sèvres cups, each one painted by hand.

At her exclamation Napoleon smiled and said in quite his old tone, "Ah, Mees Betsee, so you like sweets! That is because your disposition has need of them. You shall eat a whole tower of the centerpiece all yourself. Piron will be charmed. He thinks his skill is not well appreciated. Tell me, the black cook at the Briars could not contrive such a marvel as that, could he?"

"Jamais!" exclaimed Betsy and Jane with one breath. Such spontaneous enthusiasm evidently gave pleasure.

From that moment on the two girls were less aware of the Emperor and more aware of the friend. As soon as they left the table their host began showing them his treasures. First among them were several paintings of his son—the little King of Rome. One artist had presented the rosy infant cradled in the helmet of Mars under the French flag, with a crown in his tiny hand.

"What does that mean?" asked Betsy.

"That he would reap the reward of his father's conquests and be a power in the world." Napoleon sighed and picked up a miniature. "Doubtless this is nearer the truth."

A laughing child of four in long white satin breeches and frilled blouse sat astride a lamb. The two sisters exclaimed over his beauty. Next was a painting covering the top of a superb snuffbox. It represented the angelic-looking little prince kneeling before a crucifix with eyes raised to heaven. Beneath was lettered in French: "I pray God for my father, my mother and my country."

Jane went into raptures over the portrait. But Betsy could not speak. She recalled that Marie Louise had fled to Vienna with her son before her husband set out for Elba and had refused even to write to him afterwards. Consequently this father could not have seen his lovely boy for more than a year and a half. Watching the sad face bent above the snuffbox, she seemed to hear him ask, "Shall I ever see him again?"

Sumptuous portraits of Empress Marie Louise were exhibited next. Napoleon seemed pleased by the admiration of his guests. But suddenly he exclaimed, "Now I shall show you the most beautiful woman in the world." And he took from its velvet case a miniature in a magnificent frame.

Betsy looked at the small head standing out so proudly against the ivory background. Even Miss Laura Wilks had not such delicacy of feature and coloring. "Oh," she cried. "Who is that enchanting creature, monsieur?"

"My sister Pauline. Although a devotee of pleasure, she is as warm and sweet as she is fair. Next to Madame Mère she is the member of my family who has always been closest to me. She came to see me in my kingdom of Elba. Who knows—perhaps she might visit me here."

Gravely he packed away the treasures in the carved coffer that held them. Then he sprang to his feet. "Look!" he cried with an obvious effort at gaiety, "how quiet my little page has become, Mademoiselle Betsee. He is jealous because I have taken all your attention with my art exhibition. Be kind to him. He longs to give you a kiss, I know."

"He longs in vain, then," said the girl indignantly. But she got to her feet uneasily and moved as far from the others as she could.

Emanuel Las Cases smiled in an embarrassed fashion. But he made no resistance when his master flung an arm about him and pushed him toward Betsy. "Eh, bien, mon petit, faint heart never won fair damsel. Seize your opportunity. Give her a kiss. I shall hold her hands to prevent her from scratching out your eyes."

With a movement of cat-like swiftness Napoleon had sprung across the room, caught Betsy's wrists and pinioned her arms behind her. Flushed and laughing, the boy obediently leaned forward. Betsy closed her eyes in help-

[84]

less rage and shame. Then first on one cheek, then on the other, she felt the touch of soft lips. She caught a faint odor of eau de cologne and a pair of light hands gently pressed her shoulders. How utterly surprising! This was very pleasant! It flashed through her that some-day she might actually long to be kissed—by a lover.

But this was a liberty! Her eyelids flew up. "I hate you!" she gasped in a fury. "You are a thief!" She turned on her laughing captor. "And you! You are outrageous!" As soon as her hands were freed, she began scrubbing her cheeks with her handkerchief to erase the imper-tinence.

Everyone was laughing at her discomfiture. But Jane evidently felt a little pity. She proposed at once that they all go down to the bungalow and finish the evening with whist. The plan was accepted and at once the group of five started down the path. Betsy, still nursing her grievance, came on last and slowly. Then she quickened her pace. She had thought of a revenge. Just as the four figures ahead of her reached the steepest part of the de-scent, she ran swiftly forward and gave Emanuel a ter-rific push. He was hurled against Jane who fell forward with hands extended upon the shoulders of Las Cases and so sudden was the impact that he, in turn, lurched against Napoleon. The latter staggered, but kept his feet. Shriek-ing with delighted laughter Betsy thought to herself, "They are just like a lot of ninepins."

"How dare you, Miss Balcombe! This is unforgivable." Las Cases steadied Jane and leaped up to snatch Betsy by the shoulders. "You ought to be punished for this, you little hoyden." In his fury he flung her hard against the rocky bank.

"Oh, oh!" wailed the girl in pain. "Help! Monsieur l'Empereur! He has hurt me."

Perhaps it was the impulsive use of his title that really moved Napoleon to come to her aid. At any rate he strode up the path and pinioned Las Cases' arms from behind. "Never mind. Do not cry. I have him now and you may punish him."

Without stopping to weigh the matter of justice, Betsy scrambled to her feet and boxed the small man's ears with all her might. Napoleon roared with laughter. Suddenly he released the unhappy Las Cases. "Now run," he cried, "and if she catches you, Betsy has leave to strike you again." Off they went, Las Cases sprinting down hill, the girl after him, and pursuing them both, the jolly boom of heartfelt laughter.

Both the Chamberlain and his son managed to disappear into the twilight shadows. But when the others entered the house Mrs. Balcombe graciously took a hand at whist and seemed incurious about the amused glances her guest kept shooting at her younger daughter. When the game was over, however, and the girls were beginning to prepare for bed, Jane came into her sister's room and sternly reproached her for her conduct.

Betsy took it meekly. Finally she said, "But, Jane, in all justice you must admit that the whole thing was really Boney's fault. He loves to get me into a temper. And he deliberately set us all against one another. I suppose I ought to feel very chagrined, especially with my shoulder bruised. But I don't. For Boney seemed to enjoy the row; and before it happened he had been so sad."

Jane regarded her with misgiving. "Dear me, I do hope, Betsy, you are not going to become an unreasonable partisan like that mad Huff. I agree that no one so interesting as General Bonaparte has ever come into our lives. But I shouldn't want to forget all my manners just to amuse him. If you are as naughty as that again I shall certainly tell mamma. You'd do well to reflect once in a while that this man was our country's mortal enemy."

After she had gone Betsy stood for a long time at the window. But her reflections were not of the sort recommended by her sister. Neither did she relive the tempestuous scenes of the evening. Out of the still, fragrant warmth came floating toward her images from another day and another land. The miniature of Marie Louise in her ermine cloak, the handsome table trappings, the ceremonial airs of the lackeys—all had conjured up for the girl's imagination a vanished splendor. For the first time she fixed her mind upon the personal glamour which must have surrounded Napoleon—the palace buzzing with adulation, couriers speeding with his messages, people cheering in the streets when he appeared, beautiful women like his sister honored when he smiled upon them. To think of such a man living in one room now and dependent for company upon that little dried bean, Las Cases! How could he ever be gay?

Perhaps the unconscious effect of such pictures made Betsy more eager than ever to divert the exile. At any rate the very next day she was again in disgrace with Las Cases. It all came about through a complaint and a compliment. Resolving to be sedate as a nun, the girl went up to the pavilion in the afternoon. She meant to administer a gentle protest to her voluntary professor of French. For he had told her father that she had failed that morning to hand in her exercise and Mr. Balcombe had sternly reprimanded her for laziness. She thought it most unkind of one she claimed as a friend to give her away.

A busy scene presented itself in the arbor. In one corner little Frank was quietly sitting, sorting a pack of playing cards. Las Cases was correcting manuscript. At the large table General Gourgaud was sitting writing away as hard as he could and, pacing up and down nearby, was the stocky figure of Napoleon. He looked tired and hot, but was dictating in a loud voice.

"The batteries continued their fire all night," he was saying, "and at break of day the English fleet was seen out at sea." Seeing Betsy's approach, he stopped and held out a welcoming hand. "Bon! Here comes an interruption to my account of the siege of Toulon. General Gourgaud will be happy to greet you, Mees Betsee. He has been writing for an hour and must have a cramp in his hand."

"Mais, non, mon Empereur! I am not at all fatigued. It is a fine story you have told." Gourgaud looked at the intruder with a somewhat hostile expression.

"Eh bien, but I am," retorted his chief and sank into a seat near Frank. He waved to Betsy to sit near him and said to her with a malicious twinkle, "I presume your father gave you the scolding you deserved."

Before she could reply Frank got down from his chair and came to hold up a card for Napoleon's inspection. The pack presented to him by Dr. O'Meara was decorated by a cartoon very popular in England. "Look," cried the boy, "the back of this card is called the Grand Mogul and father says that means you, Boney."

"Boney! Moi?" Napoleon took up the card and examined it. "Je ne comprends pas! What does Boney mean?"

Betsy was amazed. Could he really never have heard the name which the English had been using all these years? "Boney is short for Bonaparte," said she.

But Las Cases came up to join in. In French he explained the literal meaning of the word Boney. As Napoleon listened his expression of bewilderment deepened. "But, mon dieu, nobody could call me a boney person," he protested.

As he spoke he spread out his hand and Betsy seized it in both hers. "Look," she said teasingly, "how small and plump and dimpled and white it is. This hand never held a sword—I'm sure of it."

"You think not?" The hand waved imperiously. "Come into my salon with me and I will show you one of my prized gifts, a sword as beautiful as it is deadly."

In another minute they were standing before a secretary from which Napoleon lifted a magnificent velvet case. From it he took a sword in a gleaming tortoise-shell scabbard, and with one swift movement grasped the golden handle, drew the blade from the sheath and whirled it above his head. In that attitude of a cavalryman about to charge, he looked suddenly young and unconquerable—perhaps as he had looked at Toulon.

Satisfied by Betsy's awed expression, the swordsman dropped his arm and laid the weapon across the table for her inspection. Here, she thought, was one more evidence of an imperial world where rich gifts from princes had been lavished upon this conquering hero. Exquisitely wrought in the shape of a fleur-de-lis was the golden handle. Betsy ran her finger along the bright blade. Then suddenly she snatched up the sword and made a quick pass at her companion.

He leaped backward. "Look out! C'est dangereux!" he cried.

"Your life is in my hands!" she sang out, advancing a step. "Vengeance is mine for your tale-telling to my father. You wanted me punished. Now it's your turn."

Round and round she swung the sword. Farther and farther backed her victim. He said no word, but his eyes, fastened on her hand, were eloquent of his expectation of some accident. "Tremble, sir!" she cried in wild exultation. Here was a situation to make even the great Duke of Wellington envious.

There came the sound of running feet. Las Cases looked in at the window and grew ashen. "Drop it! Drop it! Wicked girl! You might do the Emperor harm."

"I intend to kill him," she replied gleefully and with a lunge brought the sword point within an inch of the well-rounded white waistcoat. "He is a traitorous friend."

For another instant which must have seemed long to the others, the girl spun that deadly point in a threatening arc. Then the spell was broken by the sound of Jane's voice outside. "Betsy! I have news for you."

Her arm dropped, and with a bow she tendered Napoleon the handle of the sword. He took it, smiling a little. With a firm headshake he stopped Las Cases, bursting into the room and striding toward the assailant. As he calmly put the weapon away, he called out to Jane to enter and report her news.

The newcomer looked curiously from Betsy's excited face to the white wrath of Las Cases. "What has been going on here?" she asked. "More bad tricks?"

"Just a little sword practice," replied Napoleon swiftly. "Ah, there is Gourgaud also. Come in, Baron, you arrive not a moment too soon." He chuckled and tweaked Betsy's ear. "Tell us, Mademoiselle Jeanne, is your news good?"

"I think so." She waved an envelope. "We have just received an invitation from Sir George Cockburn to a ball he is giving at the Castle. Even you are invited, Betsy. But I don't know whether father will let you go. Think, monsieur le Général, she has never been to a ball."

Betsy remained silent. Did she really wish to go? No party could be as exciting, as unique, as the hours she spent right in this spot. Perhaps if everyone went away except her, she could spend the evening with Boney and he would talk to her and tell her about his wonderful life.

"What is it, mademoiselle?" asked Gourgaud wonderingly. "Don't you think your father will permit you to accept? You must beg the Emperor to persuade him. Voilà, sire. She will meet there the handsome young officer whose portrait she has drawn." Laughing, he held out a sketch. "I found it in the arbor and recognized it at once. The Honorable George Carestairs. I met him yesterday."

The leap of Betsy's heart brought the blood to her cheeks in a furious blush. "So that is his name!" she exclaimed. And she paid no attention to the laughter which burst out all about her. Already she was tripping through a reel on the arm of the haughty young man while envious glances from all the other girls were cast upon the handsome and graceful pair. What would his voice be like? Would he pay her compliments? She dropped a deep curtsey to Napoleon and looked up at him mischievously. "Monsieur le Général, I have just spared your life. In return, will you get me to the ball?"

6

CONQUEST AT A BALL

"So this is to be your first ball, Betsy! I do hope you won't find it dull. Disappointments are hard—especially for the young. But certainly Admiral Cockburn is sparing nothing to make the occasion a success."

The charming voice, tinged with melancholy, seemed exactly in keeping with the personality of Madame Bertrand. Betsy thought the tall, slim visitor far the most distinguished woman she had ever met. Later Mrs. Balcombe's phrase, "quite the last word in Paris fashions, my dears," caused her to recall the frock of green bombazine with pleated neckpiece of white and a square hat garnished with green and white plumes. But at the time the girl had eyes only for the high-bred face shadowed with sadness. Madame Bertrand, she knew, was of aristocratic English parentage. How strange for one who had perched on the pinnacle of fortune to find herself here in this remote spot, sipping tea under the Balcombes' pepper trees!

Shyly Betsy responded to the visitor. "I'm sure I shall not be disappointed, ma'am. I am only too grateful that

General Bonaparte persuaded my father to let me go."

"Did he?" Madame Bertrand smiled and turned to Mrs. Balcombe. "The Emperor is really kind. I am often struck, also, by his intense love of freedom. He was deeply disturbed a little while ago when General Gourgaud told him that this morning a slave girl had been sold in the Jamestown market. Such a thing is terrible to contemplate, is it not? Have you slaves, Madam?"

"No, indeed. My husband is far too liberal. We hire from his owner one old Malay slave, but I think he is happy here. Old Toby has become quite devoted to General Bonaparte. He gave him a key to the small fruit garden and seems delighted to have him pick whatever he likes—a privilege not granted any member of our family, I assure you."

Smiling faintly, Madame Bertrand set down her teacup and gathered up her gloves. "How thankful we should be that England is about to abolish the slave trade. Admiral Cockburn tells me that Parliament was so occupied with debates on that subject all last year that very little interest was taken in the fate of Europe. The treaty of Vienna was practically that of Lord Castlereagh alone."

She broke off, sighed and looked about her a little dazedly. Probably she realized afresh, thought Betsy, how far away was that world of great affairs. Presently the group was joined by Count Henri Grattien Bertrand who came down from the pavilion to escort his wife back to Jamestown. Betsy thought the bald, smallish man rather an insignificant husband for such a woman. Yet the way his face lighted up when she took his arm spoke eloquently of his very real devotion. Moreover, his manner of saying farewell to Mrs. Balcombe had a true French elegance.

At the rose hedge Madame Bertrand turned and, calling Betsy to her, said, "My dear, at the ball I mean to introduce to you a very haughty young Ensign, the Honorable George Carestairs. I count on you to pierce the scorn he seems to entertain for the frail sex."

She ended with a soft laugh in a minor key. And with this sound in her ears, checking the whirl of her thoughts, the girl walked slowly back to the others.

"What did Madame say to you? Why are you blushing?" asked Jane.

But Betsy, pretending not to hear, bent over her mother's chair. "Please, mother, come with me now—at once—while I try on my new frock. I so want it to be quite perfect for tomorrow night."

Exchanging a smile with her elder daughter, Mrs. Balcombe obligingly arose. "Jane, dear," said she, "kindly see that the decanters are filled and the little cakes ready. General Bonaparte is coming down to play whist tonight and as we have dinner guests there will be no further time to give instructions."

Betsy quite resented that evening. She would have preferred to be alone dreaming of the ball. Instead she had to endure the conversation of the Bennets and the Hodsons at dinner and play accompaniments afterwards for Mrs. Bennet. The lady's piercing soprano was always a strain on her nerves, but doubly so on this occasion. For in the midst of the concert Napoleon was announced. He insisted that the music should go on. Then he sat where he could flick at Betsy glances which plainly told her what silent ridicule he was heaping on the singer. Worse still, he afterwards praised the performance with such exaggerated compliments that Betsy could hardly keep her countenance.

When the guests left they carried with them their host and hostess to attend a party at the Skeltons' in Jamestown. Graciously Napoleon waved aside their protests and assured them that with Las Cases and the two young ladies, the whist table would be complete.

Hardly had the others gone when, with a deviltry which amused even Las Cases, Napoleon began in a vile falsetto to imitate Mrs. Bennet's high trills. Betsy laughed until her sides ached and even Jane entered into the mimicry with great spirit, crying, "Bravo! Simply divine!"

Suddenly, however, the older girl stopped laughing and said reproachfully, "General Bonaparte, you are very disconcerting. We have been taught never to be rude about mother's guests or to make fun of them."

"Right, quite right, mademoiselle," he replied. "Madame Bennet as a person is doubtless worthy of all respect. But as a musician—non! In the field of art one can with a clear conscience make merry over the fakirs. Mon dieu, what execrable singing!"

With that he marched over to the card table, sat down and bade the others join him. But his roguish high spirits made it impossible for him to play the game seriously. He kept peeking at the cards of his opponents and brazenly plotting the right leads with Jane who was his partner.

Betsy sprang to her feet with flashing eyes. "You are a cheat. I will not play any more. It is abominable!"

"What? *I* cheat?" returned Napoleon with such a good imitation of haughty innocence that for a second the girl was abashed. "Never was injustice greater. But before we go on with the game, mon enfant, show me the dress you are to wear tomorrow night. I must learn how charming you are going to look."

Immediately criticism was forgotten. Betsy was all radiance. "Do you really want to see it, sir?" Fleetly she ran up the stairs and returned in a moment with the beautiful creation over her arm. Mousseline de soie it was, with satin rosebuds fastened at waist and shoulders and scattered over the skirt. Proudly the girl spread it out. "N'est-ce pas une jolie robe?"

"Oui, oui. Bee-you-ti-ful. Molta bella. Exquise! Even you will look angelic in it, little bad one. Leave it there for us to enjoy while we continue the game." He dealt the cards saying with a wink for Las Cases, "This time we shall play for a reward. I am betting a napoleon." He clanked the gold piece down.

Betsy brought a coin from the top drawer of a commode. "I will wager my pagoda. But this time, no cheating."

"What an idea! Certainly not." But, although his tone was indignant, Napoleon immediately began again to peek at cards and make signals to Jane. The more Betsy protested, the more he laughed. Finally, he jumbled all the cards together, tossed the coins into Betsy's lap and shouting, "I'll punish you for calling me a cheat!" he snatched up the mousseline frock and bounded out of the house.

"Ma robe! Ma belle robe!" shrieked Betsy. She hurled

herself in pursuit. But in the moonlight she saw the imperial white breeches striding up the path at great speed and when she reached the pavilion, the door was bolted. To her knocking and shouts came no response.

Disconsolately she returned. "Oh, Jane, what shall I do?" she wailed. "Boney will certainly crush my flowers. Perhaps he won't even give back my frock. Then I couldn't go to the ball." She began to sob.

Although Jane reassured her at the time, the entire next day passed without a sign from Napoleon. In the morning he went for a long ride and on his return he was closeted for hours with his staff of four—Gourgaud and Counts Monthalon, Bertrand, and Las Cases. Later Colonel Bingham joined the conference. Mr. Balcombe, saying he believed some important discussion was taking place, refused to disturb them by sending a servant to inquire about the ball dress.

In the late afternoon Dr. O'Meara came riding up. As Napoleon's personal physician appointed by the Admiralty, he visited his charge every few days and often stopped to chat with Mr. Balcombe. Catching sight of a girlish figure on the veranda, he dismounted and called out, "I hear you are attending the ball tonight, Miss Betsy. I trust you will honor me with your hand in the lancers."

Piteously the girl gazed up into the pleasant Irish face. "Oh, Dr. O'Meara, Boney has hidden my ball dress to tease me. Do persuade him to send it back. I don't know what I'm going to do."

Heartily the doctor laughed. "Oh, it is only his joke. I am sure you need not be anxious, and for my part, I am very glad that his mood is so merry. Perhaps it means that those complaints of food, restrictions, and everything else which the Governor and the Admiral received today are not so serious after all. I'll see what I can do to restore the stolen goods, Miss Betsy, rest assured." Lifting his hat he led his horse up the path.

For an instant the girl stood in deep reflection. Then she ran into the study. Her mother was sitting at the window, busy with her crocheting, and by another window her father stood looking out.

"Father," she cried, "aren't you in charge of the supplies used at the pavilion?"

He turned with a quick frown. "Yes, child. I was appointed head of the commissary for the entire French colony."

"Well, then, why don't you send the Emperor plenty of good things to eat? Dr. O'Meara says there have been complaints. I am very angry at Boney for taking my dress, but I should hate to have him starve. Why are you so stingy?"

Anger flashed red in the face above her. "Don't enter into questions of which you know nothing, daughter," said he sternly. "A definite allowance has been made by the British Government and I am not supposed to exceed it. Three different households, a number of children and a great many servants use up supplies very quickly. I do all I can."

"But why doesn't the Governor or the Admiral do something then—order more supplies, for instance?"

"Betsy," chided her mother with some sharpness, "you

are impertinent. Don't annoy your father with questions which I should never dream of asking."

"But I want to know," she cried passionately. "Boney and I are friends. I hate his having to make complaints. I can't bear to think of his not being comfortable and happy."

Mr. Balcombe put his hand under her chin and gazed earnestly down at her. His expression took her by surprise. For he no longer looked angry, but pitying as if something threatened her which he felt helpless to prevent. What could it be? Suddenly, without a word, he dropped his arm and walked straight out of the room.

Dinner was early that evening. For the Balcombes had many preparations to make. They kept three servants busy bringing cans of hot water and packing tin cases with party dresses, slippers, fans and shawls. Even Mr. Balcombe had his kit containing dancing pumps and a fine broadcloth coat. For, since everyone at St. Helena went to parties on horseback, ball costumes had to be donned in the dressing-rooms after arrival. With nervous fingers Betsy collected her possessions and fidgeted before the mirror while old Sarah did her hair. Every instant she expected Napoleon's lackey with her frock. Why didn't he send it? How could he be so heartless? As she asked herself these questions she had to wink back the tears.

At last Mrs. Balcombe stood in the doorway. A lace scarf was wound about her beautifully arranged hair and in her hand was a riding whip. "Well, darling," she said, "the horses have been brought around and it is time to leave. What are you going to do? The choice seems to lie between wearing your plainer dress or staying at home.

It's a very sweet little frock, so why not make the best of it? You don't want to miss all the fun."

"Oh, mother!" Before Betsy's eyes passed pictures of Madame Bertrand shaking her head in disappointment and of young Carestairs greeting so dowdy a lady with a contemptuous smile. Was it really any use to go? In a choked voice she said, "Boney threatened to punish me for calling him a cheat. But, mother, he did cheat. It doesn't seem fair. It isn't like him. I'm sure it isn't."

At this the same pitying expression she had seen on her father's face met her again. "My pet," said Mrs. Balcombe gently, "you must learn that people often do disappointing things which one cannot understand. Remember that General Bonaparte is more than three times your age. He has been the greatest figure of his day. And he is foreign. How can you expect to understand such a nature? I think it quite likely that he is revenging himself for the liberties you have taken. Come now, dear, we must get off."

Old Sarah handed the girl her bonnet. "That Boney," she growled angrily, "I always declared he was devil. You better remain away from him, Miss Betsy."

"Hush! It isn't true." Snatching her hat, Betsy went down to the garden.

Already two little black boys had shouldered the tin boxes and Jane was in the saddle. It was, indeed, the last moment. Watching her mother being helped upon her horse, Betsy slowly crossed the lawn. Her father was holding her stirrup in readiness. Suddenly he dropped it and began to clap his hands. At the same instant the girl uttered a shriek of delight. For around the corner of the house strode Marchand, the valet, and across his extended arms lay the mousseline frock, unwrinkled and exquisite as ever.

"The Emperor's compliments, mademoiselle," said Marchand gravely. "He hopes you will do le Baron Gourgaud the honor of dancing with him."

That was a favor Betsy found easy to grant. He was the first man at whom she smiled after she had greeted her host, the tall resplendent Admiral. Before her mother or Jane could lead her about the candle-lit, flower-decked ballroom for formal presentations, she was off on the Frenchman's arm finding her place in a square dance. He introduced her to two others in the set, Count and Countess Montholon. She thought them both surprisingly young and good-looking, but in spite of the wonderful emeralds she wore, the Countess seemed commonplace compared to Madame Bertrand.

For more than an hour Betsy never stopped dancing for an instant. Friends of her father hurried up with cordial greetings and the reminder that only recently they had dandled her as an infant on their knees. Lieutenants from the fort whom she had met through Jane begged for the privilege of her hand. Sir George Bingham presented to her several officers from his regiment. But as she made her bows and pirouettes, happily conscious of her pretty frock and the admiring glances of her partners, Betsy had but one thought back of her radiant eyes. "Where was *he,* and when would Madame Bertrand present him?"

Finally, as the Fifty-third Regiment band crashed out the end of a quadrille, the girl caught sight of Madame Bertrand's tall figure beside Gourgaud. Betsy turned to her partner. "Major Fehrzen, let us join the Governor's group over there. I promised to speak to Madame Bertrand and perhaps," she added with an arch glance, "you might possibly enjoy a moment with Miss Laura Wilks."

It was not, however, until they were shaking hands and exchanging curtsies all around that Betsy realized that someone stood on the other side of Madame Bertrand. One flick of an eye took in his height and the gold epaulettes broadening still further his big shoulders. Before her heart had skipped a beat, before she could put back the curl fallen against her hot cheek, she heard his name pronounced. The hand she had automatically held out was brushed by the lips of the bowing young man. Tongue-tied, she stood shyly looking past his shoulder while Madame complimented her upon her dancing and her appearance. Panic had dispersed all the wiles she had carefully planned.

Nevertheless, as the music struck up again she found herself, without knowing how, moving beside the Honorable George Carestairs into place for the reel. Her glance found him smiling. How practiced and deft he was. He made the other men seem like louts. To sink deeper into the illusion, she moved with half-closed eyes until the music stopped. For she knew that the end of the dance was the end of a dream.

"Shall we stroll on the terrace to cool off, Miss Balcombe?" The voice was deep and assured.

She took her partner's arm with a feeling of terror. What on earth could she say to interest a man who had been everywhere, known everyone? She felt shut in by the smallness of St. Helena and of her own experience. Hardly had they proceeded a yard across the lawn when she observed approaching them Jane and another girl, each with a uniformed escort. The glances of surprise and envy she received sent her anxiety a pitch higher. How could she possibly charm the magnificent creature striding beside her?

"This is a pleasant ball, Miss Balcombe."

"You think so? But you must have attended such fine ones in London."

"Upon my honor, no. Only a few balls in the country where my people live down in Lincolnshire. You see, my father had hardly bought me a post in my regiment when it was sent off to India. Then I fought a bit in Spain and returned to England just in time for Sir George to pack me off here. So I've had small time for society."

"Ah, but you have seen the world." She glanced up with eyes which had caught a gleam of the bright moonlight.

The aquiline profile of the Honorable George became a pleased face bent down upon her. "True. But you don't even have to travel," he replied. "Look how the world comes to you. Admiral Cockburn, for example, is a very important man—served in the American War quite recently, you know. He helped burn the Yankee capitol at Washington."

Betsy looked her surprise. "But I thought England was not proud of that. The *London Times* certainly deplored the action."

A gleam of white teeth showed in his amused smile. "Oh, yes, the opinion of stay-at-homes! Although, upon my word, it is amazing that young ladies read the sheet! I belong to the school which thinks all is fair in love and war." He drew her hand a little farther into the crook of his arm and pressed the fingers gently. "A man must conquer so that he may not be conquered."

Wouldn't Jane say that the Ensign was flirting? As Betsy finally mounted the step to return to the ballroom, she looked full at her escort for the first time. Yes, her sketches had not been exaggerated. He was, indeed, remarkably handsome. But oh, how she wished she could shake even a little of his easy self-confidence.

"Oh, here you are, Miss Betsy!" Just inside the door of the Castle Dr. O'Meara pounced upon her. "Your mother requested me to look for you and I might add that several officers have shown the same anxiety." He grinned amiably at Carestairs.

"Tell them all," he replied masterfully, "that the young lady is in excellent hands." He was urging Betsy gently toward the middle of the ballroom where a new quadrille was forming.

But with impetuous violence the girl withdrew her hand from the blue coat-sleeve. "I have promised Dr. O'Meara this dance." As she took leave of the Ensign by dropping a brief curtsey, she was delighted to see an astonished frown wrinkle his sunburned forehead.

Not until long after midnight did she catch another glimpse of Carestairs. At the elaborate supper table set up in the hall of the Castle she saw the young officer in Admiral Cockburn's party with a number of older people. He presented a picture of well-bred boredom. With satisfaction her quick eyes noted that, although he sat beside the lovely Laura Wilks, he left her entertainment to the man on her left. Still more pleasing was what happened when the long, gay repast was at an end. As the attractive Major Fehrzen, who had been her partner for supper, drew back her chair for her to rise, a tall form bent over her.

"Miss Balcombe remembers, I am sure, that she promised to dance the next figure with me."

At the sound of that voice she looked up so quickly that she caught the Ensign winking at the Major. He had the grace to blush then and send her a look of real entreaty. It amazed her and made her feel confident and cool, like a great lady. Donning a look of indifference as she might have put on a bonnet, she said, "It is well you reminded me." But with considerable haste she laid her hand on his arm and stepped with him across the floor.

Before the party was over several things occurred to open up pleasing vistas. When Betsy presented the young man to her father and mother they asked him to call and he gravely accepted. Moreover, Miss Wilks invited her to tea and said with a teasing smile, "I have reason to believe that Mr. Carestairs is coming." Finally, as she was changing her clothes for the ride back, Madame Bertrand came into the dressing-room for her cloak.

"All my felicitations, my dear," she whispered to Betsy. "You have made an excellent beginning."

The ride home was through a fog which had drifted in from the sea. To Betsy the weird shapes of trees and rocks in the ghostly moonlight seemed quite in keeping with a world strangely changed merely by going to a ball. She took no part in the lively talk which passed between her parents and Jane. She was busy etching deeper in her memory every line of a sunburned face and of a figure in uniform. Her ears hummed with the murmur of a low voice saying, "When may I come and see the sunlight in your hair?"

The sudden prancing of her pony reminded her that they must be nearing home. "Steady, Tom," she murmured, reining him in. But, when they reached a certain wide spot in the road, he plunged past the others and sprinted up the last lap toward the Briars' gate.

"Halt and give the parole!"

Out of mist and shadows thrust stern challenge and glint of bayonet. A row of figures woodenly blocked the way. As the girl pulled her pony to a quivering stop, she heard behind her Mr. Balcombe sing out the password. Instantly the human barricade dissolved and the gate opened before the riders. More startling than the sentry's cry, however, had been a thought shouted in Betsy's mind. "Boncy!" She had forgotten him completely. Forgotten the most exciting person in the world! Slipping from the saddle at the corner of the veranda, she looked with astonishment at the spot where she had waited in anguish for her ball gown. That was only six hours ago, but it seemed six years.

Next morning the girl wakened to a fresh sense that life was packed to bursting. As she lay stretching a body that felt both light and pleasantly weary from dancing so late, she caught the sound of excitement below—voices calling and the rhythm of hoof-beats. At breakfast she discovered the cause. An English ship had arrived with mail. Mrs. Balcombe, reading a pile of it, tossed bits of information to her daughters. They listened, crunching toast, to the news about Granny and friends familiar to them only in name.

"Oh, how far away they all are!" said Mrs. Balcombe with sudden tears in her eyes. "They speak of Waterloo but evidently knew nothing of General Bonaparte's being sent here."

Her daughters did not answer. They were giggling over an ingenious cartoon of Boney which had been mailed to Betsy. The latter only looked up when Baron Gourgaud came striding past the window. His head was down and, like a sulky boy, he was kicking at the pebbles in his path. When she saw him later on the veranda, he burst out with the reason for his black mood. "No message from my mother!" he exclaimed. "I had to bring the mail up to the Emperor and Las Cases received five letters. It's like his luck. He gets everything. He was never in as many battles as I. Yet now he seems to be far more important."

In astonishment the girl regarded the young fellow. Who would expect a grown-up person to be so petty? "You are jealous of Las Cases," she said accusingly.

"And why not?" He spread out both hands in a Gallic gesture. "The Emperor is all I have. I am lonely. All the others have children to love; two have their wives with them. I have but a single devotion—mon Empereur. I shouldn't mind so much Bertrand being preferred to me. After all, he has known the Emperor for a long time. But Las Cases! And Montholon! They have no superior claims."

To divert her companion she asked, "Where is your Emperor this morning?"

"He is taking a walk. Dr. Warden is with him. The doctor is writing a book about his trip to St. Helena and everything the Emperor told him on board the *Northumberland*. I do not like him. I shall not come off well in his book. Neither will you. He says that he never knew such a spoiled child as you."

"I?" She sprang to her feet like a cat whose tail has been pinched. "I am not a child." How could Gourgaud use the term after seeing her at the ball? "And I am certainly not spoiled."

"Non?" The General looked at her with a malicious smile. "What about all the monkey tricks you have played on the great Emperor? He spoils you terribly. However, I suppose it amuses him. It keeps his mind from all the petty and irritating things that happen. And the great injustice done him."

"What is that?" Betsy had never talked so long with a member of Napoleon's staff and was intensely curious.

"Diable! That he came to the British of his own free will, asking to be the guest of a generous foe and was packed off here to this horrible place to be spied on and guarded every moment."

Yes, she had heard that before. Mr. Huff was always talking in that fashion. But was it true? Was it just? What could the government have done? Betsy felt bewildered and sad and somehow guilty, as if she too were to blame. When Gourgaud, his eyes on her face, suddenly proposed that they find the Emperor and shoo Dr. Warden away, she started off beside him with relief. In Napoleon's presence she never felt this stormy air charged with electricity. It was his followers who gave it off—Madame Bertrand so unhappy, Las Cases always disapproving, Gourgaud forever upset.

They had not gone far down the rocky path into the ravine when they met Dr. Warden scrambling up. "The General is in splendid humor," he called out. His French had a strong English accent. "I have had to answer a thousand new questions. He seems in excellent health, but he does not like St. Helena."

"How strange that is," barked Gourgaud. Lifting his hat, he pushed past the other.

Betsy followed him. But, looking back, she saw the surgeon staring after them in bewilderment. There it was again, she thought—that conflict! Would there never more be harmony on the island? People seemed to think of nothing except enmities. The French against the English and within those divisions constant antagonism. Where would it lead? She felt a horrid uneasiness.

When they came upon Napoleon standing on a great rock overlooking the ravine, Betsy saw Gourgaud's face freeze to behold Las Cases with him. But she herself was caught up in gay greetings and a fire of maddening questions. How had she behaved at the ball? Had she tried to monopolize Baron Gourgaud or had she shared him with the charming Mademoiselle Wilks? Did all the English ladies drink gin and brandy for supper? Why was she skipping lessons this morning? Had she had any love letters from England?

His prodding succeeded in making her fairly dance with irritation. "I had no love letters," she retorted, "but

I did receive something from grandmother which I have a good mind to show you." She thrust her fingers into the crocheted bag swinging at her wrist, but paused.

"Show it!" As she still hesitated, Napoleon pulled her ear and repeated, laughing, "Show it, little scape-grace! I command you."

"Very well. There! See if you like it." She took from the bag the cardboard toy. It represented Napoleon in ugly caricature mounting a ladder, each step of which represented some conquered country. By pushing the strip underneath the figure could be made to climb up rung by rung until he was astride the globe on top. Then another push and at once he tumbled down head first.

For an instant Betsy was absorbed in the amusement of working the device. But abruptly she felt stricken by a deathly chill. Nobody had laughed. Nobody spoke. One scared glance showed her the three Frenchmen, with accusing eyes fixed upon her, standing motionless as stone. Napoleon's pallor had deepened. The still faces of his friends were slowly flushing with fury. She dropped her head and stuffed away the offending object. Tears of regret rose in her throat. Gourgaud was right. She was a child and spoiled. Thoughtless wickedness had prompted her to exhibit that cartoon. Without surprise she heard the angry crunch of boots as Las Cases turned on his heel and strode up the path to the Briars.

Into the succeeding silence fell a sigh. Then Napoleon said quietly, "A man must accomplish his destiny. That is my great doctrine. Eh, bien, let mine be fulfilled!"

No anger. No word of blame for her, nor for the country that reviled him. Just calm acceptance of his fate.

What power was in those simple words to make her throat so tight, to make her want to sob and cheer, both at the same time? Not even that first glimpse of him on horseback had inspired such awe.

Receiving the tribute of her eyes Napoleon smiled faintly and said, "Show us a way back through the fields, Betsy, if you please."

On the way he made Gourgaud talk a little about the vessel which had come in and teased him gently about Miss Wilks. After they had pushed their way over rocks and through giant tree ferns to the Briars' pasture, conversation became more lively. Then it stopped altogether. So did locomotion. Even breathing halted. For suddenly the invaders had come face to face with the Bennets' prize bull. Before the menace of his horns they felt small and frail.

"Quick! Over that wall!" cried Napoleon.

They ran pell mell. With a bellow of rage the bull pursued. Betsy took the wall like a thoroughbred and poised on the top to lend a hand. As the animal charged, Gourgaud waited to boost "the little Corporal" to safety. In the nick of time all three of them landed on the other side.

"Sacré Bleu, mon Empereur!" cried the young man excitedly. "What an escape! I have helped save your life for the second time!"

He had drawn himself up impressively. But Napoleon, brushing off his dusty coat, was gasping with laughter. "He is a good British patriot, that bull. He wanted to save his government the expense of keeping me."

Pleased with his joke, delighted with the adventure, Napoleon had the look of a schoolboy. Betsy, almost run-

ning to match his strides, shared his high spirits. But
Gourgaud kept pace with them in silence. The girl
glanced at his sulky face, wondered, then understood.
Napoleon had neither praised nor thanked him and the
hero was offended.

Beyond the stables they saw William Balcombe just
parting from Las Cases. Napoleon waved his hat. "We
have nearly lost our lives," he called out gaily.

Mr. Balcombe, however, bowed with grave face.
"Elizabeth," he said as she drew near, "I wish to see you
in my study."

At once she knew why. Las Cases had reported the insult she had offered his Emperor. "Oh, Granny," she
wailed inwardly, "I wish you had never sent me that cartoon." Seated beside the study table, Betsy thought she
had never seen her father look so stern.

"Can you imagine my embarrassment," he began, "to
have Count Las Cases complain of my daughter? To
think that you, who pretend to like General Bonaparte,
would treat him with discourtesy! Don't tell me you
didn't know you were insulting. What have you to say?"

"Nothing, father," she murmured, trying not to weep.
"It was wrong of me. I was sorry the moment I showed
the thing."

"Sorry! Why—why—you are absolutely not fit to as-
sociate with adults." Mr. Balcombe glared at her and
pondered the penalty. "Beginning at this moment you
shall be locked in the little cellar under the east wing
of the house—sleep and take your meals there. Perhaps
when you emerge you will think before wounding another's feelings."

Betsy made no protest. She thought she might prefer solitary confinement to the humiliation of some more public punishment. It was cool in the cellar and while the light lasted she could read a book called *Pride and Prejudice* which Miss Wilks had brought from Bath and loaned to Jane. The dinner tray was a diversion and while her candle lasted in the dark she went on reading. After it guttered out, however, she could only lie there and think. At first she reviewed the ball and other scenes in which she had played a pleasing role. But as hours passed and still sleep refused to come, she grew indignant.

"That horrid Las Cases!" she said aloud. "He has brought me to this. Why did they come here? I hate them all—even Boney! He could have put in a good—"

The girl started nervously. Wasn't that a scratching sound? There! It came again—louder—over by the wall. Now a squeal and a faint patter of tiny feet. How horrible to have no light! More squeals! Every nerve grew taut with deadly certainty. The cellar was swarming with rats. In another instant she felt them charge against the posts of her cot. She flung down her book with all her might and as the feet scurried away, she sat up and drew her slippers on. What could she do? She screamed—once—twice—three times—and listened, but no answer came. The house was still as death.

Again came the charge against the bed. Suppose they scrambled up and rushed upon her! With a terrible effort she got to her feet and running across the narrow space flung herself upon the door. It would not yield. Behind her, ever bolder, came the rats. There must be dozens of them—an army. Wildly she ran here and there. Always the creatures followed her. She felt about for a weapon. She was too desperate now for fear. Well she knew that her very life was at stake. Suddenly her groping hand touched a bottle. She hurled it at her enemies. There was a crash, silence and then a heavy scent of wine. Ah, she had won for the moment! And there was plenty of such ammunition beside her.

Once more the squeals and rush of feet came toward her through the inky dark. Again she flung a bottle. For more than an hour the contest kept up. Then, at last, dawn came stealing through the window bars and she knew that victory was hers. The squeals ceased. In the dim light she saw tails and whiskers disappearing into holes. Yet she stood there, armed and ready, until increasing brightness proved the rats had gone. Then consternation overwhelmed her. What had she done? Her father's costly wine! It trickled over the opposite wall and lay in dark pools amid the splintered glass. Oh, he would never forgive this! How could she face him now? Weakly she staggered over to her cot and fell down prone. Instantly her consciousness was blotted out. Exhaustion and the fumes of alcohol had brought her a death-like sleep.

When she awoke, it was in her own bed. She stretched and looked about. Then memory rushed back. What time was it? She couldn't believe the clock—five in the afternoon? Old Sarah must have found her and carried her upstairs. With a shudder she tried to think what her father would say to her now. Yet it was almost with relief that she saw him, just as she pulled her pillows up, come tiptoeing into the room. Better learn at once what new punishment must be undergone.

"Betsy, my darling child!" He was beside her and had gathered her into his arms. "Are you quite well now? I have been so anxious."

"Oh, father, do you know about the wine? I am so sorry. I couldn't—"

"Hush! Yes, I know. It doesn't matter. Nothing matters except that you are safe. You might have been eaten alive. My poor little girl! If I had ever known about those rats —good Lord—it makes my heart stand still. Will you forgive me for such a punishment?"

After he had gone and her mother had come in with bread and milk and a soft hand on her head, Betsy lay in blissful contemplation. What an adventure! It would be fun to tell Boney all about it and make him laugh. She still felt tired now, but in the morning she would dash up to the pavilion the first thing. And meanwhile she could dream of the Honorable George Carestairs, flirt, hero, Adonis and man of the world. Would she see him tomorrow? She thought it likely.

But these were incalculable days. Before the next morning was over, Sir George Cockburn had brought Betsy's new world crashing down.

THE PLOT THAT FAILED

Of course, there would have been no peace of mind for Betsy without her amends to Napoleon. Early on the morning after her recovery she had gone up to see him and was warmly received.

For once his manner was untinged by teasing and, after her apology had been graciously accepted, he asked briskly, "Do you know a man named Huff from whom I received a curious message yesterday?"

"Yes, monsieur. He is the tutor for Frank and Alex. Surely you have seen him about—a very young man, monsieur."

"Perhaps. So many people come and go. He writes French well for an Englishman and also differs from his compatriots in feeling I am unfairly treated."

They had been strolling through wild grass and ferns toward a little summerhouse perched on a knoll in the wavering shade of gum and pepper trees. A dewy freshness was in the air and Betsy felt tingling with life. As she turned now to look full at her companion she found him worn and pale with dark shadows beneath his eyes.

[117]

Such signs of a secret existence which she never touched always startled her. Still more strange was the expression fixed upon her with his last words.

"Mr. Huff is quite odd," she replied uneasily. "But he has always been your champion, monsieur le Général. I remember well that he was the only person on St. Helena who did not rejoice that you had left France for Elba."

"Ah—oui? That is very interesting. Why did he not?"

"He admired your genius. He wanted you to rule an united Europe and keep the peace."

They had reached the summerhouse now and Betsy was imperiously waved into a chair. Napoleon, however, stood looking out into the little valley which cuddled the Briars between somber hills. After a moment he turned about with a short laugh.

"I lament that Huff was the only inhabitant to appreciate me. For I am certain he is mad. I have told no one about the letter he left on my table addressed to my Imperial Majesty. He offered—well, I fear I should speak to your father about him. Has he never seemed to you of unsound mind?"

"What?" Betsy's eyes grew round. "Why, monsieur, he teaches the little boys very well and they work hard for him. Still he does call himself an exile and is forever criticizing the government for unfairness to you. Is that unsound?"

Again the dry laugh rattled in her ears. "For an Englishman? But certainly. A fanatic probably who might serve some good purpose in the right place, but who wastes words here."

"Well," reflected Betsy, "at least he once made me

realize some things you have done besides fight—the Code Napoléon, for example. But he is so excitable and prejudiced that he makes me feel strange. I detest him." She had drawn from her companion a grave look. Then he turned back to watch the mist upon the hillsides curling up like smoke under the hot sun rays. To his back she blurted out, "What did he write you?"

Napoleon did not turn. "The letter is burned," he said sharply. Then more gently he went on, "Do not hate that young man, Betsee. He must be sick—in the head. He will bear watching."

She sprang to her feet and stood beside him. "Oh, how confusing everything is. I don't understand. People report that you and your staff have sent many complaints to the Governor and the Admiral, but now when one Englishman feels great sympathy with you, you consider him mad. I should think you would be pleased."

In the pale face close to hers anger had blazed up and died down. Folding his arms across his breast, Napoleon said quietly, "Yes, one must be mature to judge men wisely. I know fanatics but too well. They have tried to assassinate me and tried to worship me. This Huff is of the latter sort. But think, mademoiselle, how pleased would you be if the only person who saw your side of a situation were a mere emotional boy? Such an advocate can only do me harm with the English. I should hate to have Cockburn, for example, imagine that I value sympathy without intelligence."

Betsy was concentrating. Yes, she agreed, it would be as if Mr. Huff were the only man at a ball to ask one for a dance. Her shuddering thought flew to George Carestairs' manly grace and his look of keen understanding. She wondered what Napoleon would think of him. As a sudden warm gust swept through her, she clasped her hands under her chin, saying, "And I suppose I am too young to count as a friend?"

Napoleon's arms unfolded and he patted her cheek. The gray eyes had an unwonted softness. "Ah, petite Betsee, one needs friends of all ages. We have amused ourselves well, is it not so?" Suddenly looking past her down the grassy slope, he said, "Look, Dr. Warden approaches. Without doubt he brings a new packet of questions for me to answer. Stay where you are, mademoiselle, and you will have a history lesson more important than one in the schoolroom. I shall tell your father so, if he scolds you for being absent."

The next hour was long remembered. Dr. Warden had, indeed, come with questions. When he asked them, the girl was amazed that they failed to arouse Napoleon's indignation. It was not until long afterward that she understood the great leader's shrewdness. He had clearly realized how directly he reached the English public by discussing matters of controversy with the writer of a book destined for wide circulation in England.

First of all the bold surgeon of the *Northumberland* wanted an explanation of a story Betsy well remembered. She herself had recited it one day to her playmates. It involved the poisoning of French soldiers on the fateful Eastern campaign. The girl blushed to think she had once believed Boney capable of such an atrocity and was ashamed to realize how many influential English folk must still believe it.

The Plot that Failed

With the defendant's opening words, Betsy was borne beyond all limits of the familiar. She was no longer in a summerhouse at the Briars, but on the edge of a strange, desert place. The companion, who had so often playfully pulled her ears and roared with laughter over her tricks or his own, had disappeared. In his stead was the master strategist of the world. With hands clasped behind his back or folded over his chest, he strode up and down, an old campaigner in action.

His metallic voice, uttering concise statements, intensified this image. It belonged to the man who could dictate half a dozen dispatches at once to as many couriers, ready to gallop in six different directions. It belonged to the man who once made his own terms with the Emperors of Austria and Russia and the King of Prussia. Before the girl's eyes the square figure in the green military coat had suddenly assumed the proportions of one who has created history.

In spite of her preoccupation with Napoleon himself, Betsy was well aware of what he was saying. The only foundation for the horrible story was, he declared, what happened to seven soldiers stricken with the plague in Egypt. During the French army's enforced retreat from St. Jean d'Acre to Jaffa, the wounded were either placed in boats or conveyed in make-shift carriages. But these seven men, who were near death, had been isolated to prevent the disease from spreading and they could not be moved.

Napoleon knew that the Turks, ready to rush into the abandoned town, would certainly inflict cruel treatment on the dying men. Therefore, he suggested to the army doctor that it would be an act of kindness to give them opium. The doctor, however, opposed the idea. Consequently, a rear guard was left to protect the sufferers. But fortunately they died before the Turks arrived.

Dr. Warden looked highly excited during this account. He kept constantly taking snuff and his nervous fingers spilled the powder over his frilled shirt and silk cravat. Several times he had challenged the narrator. "What, General, only seven men—not fifty-seven?" he asked. Now, at the end of the tale, he burst out, "Then, General Bonaparte, no opium was given the men?"

"No. None. Your brave and just Sir Sydney Smith was in that campaign and knows what happened." With a change of tone Napoleon added sarcastically, "It was not he but General Sir Robert Wilson who, without pretense to observation, has written copiously and erroneously on this subject."

Betsy sat in her corner of the summerhouse still as a porcelain figure. But her mind was busy as a mill wheel. Adults, she thought, always punished children for telling lies. Yet here was an English general who published lies about his foe in a book. She remembered all the pamphlets which used to come to St. Helena and which everybody believed. What villainy! She hoped with all her heart that Dr. Warden would relate the true story when he returned to England.

There followed from Napoleon a rapid account of another incident. Several hundred Turkish prisoners had been shot by the French. Not massacred, as the story went, but executed because they had broken their parole and acted the part of dangerous traitors. The speaker walked up and down, pointing over the rock-bound valley as if it were a battlefield. His terse descriptions gave the scene a ghastly vividness.

So, for the first time in her life the horrible meaning of war swept over Betsy. On this serene morning she was plunged into the thick of struggle. She choked with smoke and dust, reeled with fatigue and felt the desperate thrill of the charge. As all this happened to her, Napoleon grew unfamiliar and terrible. Suddenly she saw that to him soldiers were not really human but mere chessmen in his gigantic game. They must have known that, too. Yet they had loved him, called him "Little Corporal," been ready to die for him. How could it be? She gazed at the man of iron, repelled, fascinated, half comprehending the magnetism of so glorified a power.

Outside her musings she heard Dr. Warden shaking the story with doubting questions as a puppy shakes a rag. She noted the gracious patience with which Napoleon replied. At every point of explanation he would say earnestly, "Vous comprenez?" He appeared, quite without superior airs, to be simply glad to present his case to an eager listener.

At last, however, he remarked that this history lesson was proving too long for even a "very intelligent little girl." So Betsy was amiably dismissed. As she walked slowly toward the bungalow, she rehearsed all her conflicting impressions of the extraordinary man she had just left. She remembered how on the night of the ball her mother had told her she could not expect to understand such a nature. Then he had seemed to her so simple —either a naughty or a nice companion—though certainly never dull. Now, on the contrary, she agreed that she could never hope to fathom a being so many-sided and complex. The admission made her feel small and unimportant, yet a peculiar elation arose in her heart. It was marvelous to be close to such genius every day. He took her right behind the pages of history where great events had happened. Doubtless he would let her listen to the dictation of his memoirs and tell her about the great people he had known. How amazing to think that this friendship was only just beginning. Her only regret was that she had wasted so much time in childish romps.

At the corner of the veranda she quickened her step. She wanted to find her father and tell him about her astounding morning. He would certainly be proud to think she had won such a privilege. Even as she crossed the threshold of the door, however, a dark premonition seemed to rush out at her. In the hall the three elders were gathered, her mother, her father and Jane. They turned their heads toward her in silence and their faces stricken with pity warned her that something had happened.

"What is it?" she gasped.

Then she learned that Sir George Cockburn had been there. He had ridden up from Jamestown the day before, also, while she was still sleeping off the effects of her dreadful night in the cellar. Yesterday he had brought the news that Longwood was now ready. Today the servants were packing. Tomorrow Napoleon would be gone.

Gone? No more evenings of music and whist, no more French lessons in the arbor, no chance to go on with what was begun this morning! Betsy felt exactly as she once did when she had fallen out of the swing—hurt and giddy and sick. Her mother patted her hand and drew her gently into the drawing-room and down upon the sofa. Her father bent over her saying in his big, cheerful voice, "But, darling, you always knew he would leave us sometime." She kicked an impatient foot for answer. As if that softened the blow! Nor was Jane's intended comfort any better, telling her that he would not be far away and that they would see him often!

"Why, it's miles," she sobbed, "way off beyond the Devil's Punch Bowl. I'll never see Boney as I saw him here. And besides"—she paused for a desperate glance at the future—"it will all be so different. He won't be the same. You know it. I've lost him. And this morning—" She shut her eyes against a fresh rush of tears.

No, she couldn't be reconciled. She could only try to gather up the resolution to submit. In her mood of rebellion, the Admiral, her dazzling host at the ball, seemed to embody the inexorable force of authority that cared nothing for personal happiness. For Boney would never be happy at Longwood. She was sure of it. A bleak, dreadful place, hemmed in with bare hills, and the barracks close by to remind him every moment that he was a prisoner. He would be sad to leave the beautiful, friendly Briars!

When she saw his face that evening she knew that she was right. He came down with General Gourgaud to pay a farewell call upon his hosts. There was no gleam of the old mischief in his eye, no laughter in his throat. He seemed to be talking against time. But for all that he captivated their attention. His theme was the Empress

Josephine, of whom he had never spoken before; and he took from his pocket several lovely miniatures of her painted when she was on the throne.

"Your mother always reminds me a little of Josephine," he said to Betsy and when she repeated the compliment to Mrs. Balcombe and when the latter blushed with pleasure, he smiled. "Tell her," he added, "that until the Empress Josephine died we always remained the best of friends. She was the most graceful and feminine woman I have ever known. Everything she wore, everything she did, had an unsurpassed elegance."

Warming to his theme, he addressed Gourgaud, forgetting the others. "A characteristic trait of Josephine was her instinct to deny. Always her first word was no. And the *no* was not exactly a lie; it was a precaution, a defense."

With the suave air of a courtier, he turned to the two eagerly attentive girls. "It is just that," said he, "which differentiates us from you ladies. You are made for love and are taught to say no. We, on the contrary, glory in saying yes—even when we should not."

In a flash Betsy thought to herself, "That sounds like Mr. Carestairs. How much they would admire each other!" And for an instant she lost the weight of her sadness in a happy vision of introducing the two men and of enjoying the epigrams they would utter for her exclusive benefit.

Soon, however, the lump in her throat grew larger than ever. For the moment of parting was at hand. Compliments, thanks, cordialities, were exchanged all around. Then swiftly, as if he were determined to keep sorrowing at bay, he tweaked Betsy's ear, declared he would say good-by to them all in the morning, and was gone.

Betsy hated to wake up next day. To discover that the whole valley was a caldron of steamy mist gave her a perverse satisfaction and she envied her mother who had a bad headache and was staying in bed. Nevertheless, when toward noon she looked out of the schoolroom window at the escort assembling for the Longwood trip, she valiantly summoned resolution to go down to the lawn.

Admiral Cockburn and Count Montholon were mounted. Bertrand and Gourgaud stood beside their horses. Count Las Cases and his son, one on each side of Napoleon, were exchanging pleasantries with Jane and William Balcombe.

The instant he caught sight of her, Napoleon cried out, "Bonjour, Mees Betsee!" That jovial greeting, which would never again start the day with a promise of excitement, snapped the girl's brittle self-control and she put her handkerchief up to her eyes. The next moment she felt a playful pull at her ear.

"But no, mademoiselle! You must not weep. You must come and see me next week and very often."

She nodded, blinking back the tears. "If my father will let me."

"Balcombe!" The figure in the cocked hat turned swiftly. "You must bring Mees Jeanne and Betsee up to Longwood next week. What day shall it be? Name a day."

"Thursday, sir. I promise," smiled Mr. Balcombe.

Betsy was asked where her mother was and replied,

"She is ill, monsieur le Général; she left her regards and regrets."

"Ill? I shall go to see her." With three strides Napoleon was across the veranda and entering the hall. Following the swift black boots, Betsy ran up the stairs in time to see him step into the open doorway of her mother's room. She hovered an instant on the threshold, determined to miss nothing. Then to her joy, her mother beckoned her to enter and she understood she was needed as an interpreter.

First she translated his thanks for all Mrs. Balcombe's kindness. Next she relayed the message accompanying a gold snuffbox which he placed upon the coverlet. It was for Mr. Balcombe, a mark of esteem and friendship. Then he said something which surprised Betsy very much. It seemed so out of keeping with the ruthless warrior of whom she had had a glimpse the day before. He told them how deeply disappointed he had been to have Mr. Balcombe refuse his offer to buy old Toby, the Malay slave. "I wanted to purchase his liberty," said Napoleon. "To buy him and set him free. He has been good to me and I have grown fond of the kind old savage. But it appears that such an act would be against the governmental policy. I myself am not free enough to bestow liberty upon even the most insignificant human being—voilà!"

Long was Betsy to remember the bitterness of his expression at that moment. It was a revelation. He must have been suffering all the time, every day, every night— suffering over the loss of his freedom. The gaiety he had shown her up to the very last day at the Briars had been like a bright ribbon pinned on a cloak of inky black.

The Plot that Failed

What wrapped this man was pain. She took in the realization slowly and felt an ache deep in her bones.

"And now for you, Mees Betsee!" Napoleon's hand slid into the breast of his coat. He drew out an exquisite little bon-bon box which she had often admired. Placing it in her hand, he flashed her one of his old teasing smiles. "Perhaps you would like to present it to le petit Las Cases as a pledge of love!" Soft fingers pinched her cheek.

She caught the gift to her breast. But she could not thank him. She could only rush from the room and up the hall. Into her pillow she released the sob which was choking her. Presently she heard his boots on the stairs. Then voices below, the snorts of horses, the creak of saddles and the soft commotion of many hoofs trotting over the turf. She wanted to rise and look out, to see him riding away as he had first ridden down the avenue—was it only six weeks ago?—with his head up and his masterly hand on the reins. But she could not move. She could only lie there and weep.

When at last the tempest passed, she realized that it was suffocatingly hot. After bathing her eyes, she tiptoed downstairs to find a cooling breeze. On the way she heard Jane talking in her mother's room and the treble voices of the little boys from the nursery. She was glad no one was about. She wanted to think. Instinctively she started toward the study.

But someone was in the doorway. A figure strangely still for its startling pose. With both hands in its hair and its head thrown back till the cords of the neck stood out like rope—here was the very shape of desperation.

She merely whispered, "Mr. Huff!" But the words left her lips like a scream of fright.

Instantly the rigid head came down. Hollow eyes looked into hers. A thin hand shot out and clutched her wrist. For an instant his lips worked horribly as if his voice had died. Then he said hoarsely, "Miss Betsy, he went without a word. Now it is too late."

The girl tried to jerk her arm free but failed. "Too late for what?" she asked fearfully.

"But don't you see? I can't help him escape from *Longwood*. And it was possible from *here*. Oh, why? Why did he not answer me? Is he a coward after all? To submit to these damned jailers when he might have got away! I was the chosen instrument of aid. Now that instrument is broken. He broke it—my hero! Oh, life is too worm-eaten to bear. I have done with it—understand?"

His glance seemed to scorch her face. Then he flung her wrist away so suddenly that she reeled against the wall. When she recovered her balance she was alone. In that half instant Huff had vanished. Tottering into the study she sank into a chair. He has lost his wits, she thought, trembling with shock. What means on earth had the demented creature planned for Napoleon's escape? A shore of precipices, soldiers everywhere, no boats leaving the island without special permit and never after dark! How dreadful he was with his wild eyes and his crazy talk. Boney was right, he was sick in his head and somebody should know. Not her mother when she was ill. But surely her father would return from Longwood soon.

The Plot that Failed

It seemed hours, however, before she heard his light, firm step in the hall. And it took her some time to make him understand. He wanted to laugh her down, tell her she was seeing bogies. But when she quoted General Bonaparte's own words, he looked grave. "I suppose I had better ride over to the Bennets' place and find him," he said at last. "Say nothing of this to anyone."

Ah, what a comfort it was to place all the burden of horror on those broad shoulders! Betsy ran after her father down the hall and flung her arms about him with impulsive gratitude. Holding him a moment to know the world was sane again, she asked, "How is Longwood, father? What did Boney think of it?"

Mr. Balcombe shook his head slowly. "Well, the Admiral has doubtless done the best he could. The place is still forlorn and damp. The outlook could hardly be more dismal. General Bonaparte seemed sad. He told Cockburn politely that he was pleased with the changes, but went at once to his room, shut the door, and sent word by the valet that he wished to remain undisturbed. It's a grim business, little girl. No denying that."

When he had gone, Betsy walked through the garden out to the waterfall and sat down in the thickest shade. She looked about the familiar beauty of rocks and ferns with the feeling of a wanderer returned after many adventures. It wasn't three months since she had last brought a party of boys and girls to this place for a basket tea. Yet so much had happened meanwhile that she looked back to the occasion as if it had occurred in childhood. How exciting these weeks had been. Scene after scene rose before her mind and she realized that each one had swept her like a little boat farther out on the sea of experience. Would she drift backward now that Boney had left the Briars? Since his arrival on the island she had scarcely seen anybody of her own age. Suppose her former playmates came for an afternoon of play! No, they wouldn't be amusing now. They were all too young. It was impossible to conceive the Honorable George Carestairs enjoying childish games. Betsy stretched out on the cool ferns and closed her eyes. It was very fatiguing, she thought, to grow up so fast.

With a great start she sat upright. Hadn't she heard someone call? She must have been asleep. Long shadows told her it was late afternoon. There it was again—her name—Jane's voice almost screaming. She sprang up, climbed quickly to the top of the slope and shouted, "Here I am."

At some distance she saw Jane's figure swing around a palm tree and come toward her on the run. What could have happened? Betsy plunged swiftly through undergrowth and around big boulders until she met her sister at the edge of the Briars' land. Jane, panting for breath, flung an arm around the younger girl's shoulder and gave her something between a hug and a shake.

"We've been—so worried about you," she gasped. "Thank Heaven you're safe."

"Safe? What are you talking about? I've just been down by the waterfall."

"I know. It's quite all right. Only we were so upset. It seemed as if he might have done you some harm, as if anything might have happened. You were the last person he saw."

"Who? What harm? Tell me. Why, Jane, you're trembling. What on earth is it?"

Jane clenched her hands and swallowed hard. Then in a calmer voice she said, "Well, sister, you sent father, you know, to find Mr. Huff. Mr. Bennet had not seen him, but said he had been acting strangely of late. The two men set off together to look for him. He was not in his room, nowhere on the place. So they both came back to the Briars. They wanted to ask you more about your interview with the poor fellow, but you were gone, too. That worried them still more. So they went on searching —and—at last—oh, how can I tell you—it's horrible!"

Betsy clapped her hands to her face and a shudder shook her. "He's dead," she choked out. "He killed himself, didn't he? That was what he meant. I didn't understand. I was only frightened. Oh, Jane, how terrible!"

The other pulled down Betsy's hands and clasped them comfortingly. "Father says it might have been worse if he hadn't—if it hadn't ended at once. Mr. Huff was evidently quite insane. They went over his papers. He had been plotting Boney's escape. Can you believe it? That timid, quiet man—like a mouse! What possessed him? He had never gone near General Bonaparte. How could he have cared so much?"

Betsy felt she might find an answer to this mystery. But not now. Those telltale recollections of what young Huff had said to her from time to time were dimmed by the lurid present. She could see him in the study doorway with his head thrown back, hear him saying he was done with life. Could she have saved him if she had understood?

That evening her father talked with gentle reasonableness about the tragic episode. And after she was in bed her mother came in to read the prayers. Yet when she was alone and had blown out the candle, one haunting image after another rose up before her. As she tried to fight them off, she experienced a sharp envy of older people. They were never drawn beyond their depth into happenings. They never seemed to feel bewildered and guilty and helpless. Burying her head in the pillow to shut out the face of Mr. Huff, Betsy said to herself, "I wish I were old—quite old!"

Only three days later, however, she was very glad that she was young. Mr. Carestairs was making her glad. He had come to tea as he had promised. And for all his polite attention to her mother and father and to the Hodsons, there was a dancing something in his eyes when he looked at Betsy that gave her a plain warning.

"Just wait," that glance seemed to say. "I shall presently carry you off from all these stuffy older people and shall see you alone."

The message made easy the tiresome task of dispersing smiles and talk with the tea and cakes. But how would he do it? She took in the strength of him in his spotless uniform, marked the firm line of his chin, and waited. In the end it was very simple. He merely rose with a casual smile and bow to ask Mrs. Balcombe if Miss Betsy might show him the stables and the fruit garden. Permission was granted. And off they went.

"Please don't put on your hat," he said as they stepped on the lawn. "It isn't very hot."

She dropped her lashes, smiling. He hadn't forgotten,

then, saying that about the sunlight in her hair. How good it was after sad and dreadful days to have him here beside her, to feel merry again! When he gravely helped her over the stile on the way to the stables she was delighted and minced down steps which she took at one skip five times a day. But she must make him talk. What had he been doing, she asked.

"Upon my honor, Miss Betsy, I have had a great variety of occupations. Settling the barracks has been an irksome task. And there have been maneuvers and drill. Last night I had my first turn at the boats. That is tricky work, I assure you."

"At the boats? Pray explain, Mr. Carestairs."

"By the Admiral's orders a boat is rowed all around the island every night all night. A sort of water picket, you understand, to prevent any small craft from slipping away with the famous prisoner. It is a longish row and stiffish, what with rollers and the wind. Tiresome it is, and extraordinarily lonely out there. We keep the men singing to cheer them up. St. Helena looks fearful from a small boat on the waters at night, close under the crags. One would never guess it held a spot like this. Pretty place, the Briars. Ah, there's a good little filly out there grazing. And a white pony turning its head this way. Yours, I'll wager, Miss Betsy."

She had brought some sugar in the reticule on her wrist. So they fed the nuzzling horses and examined the stables and chatted with Peter. Presently they strolled from the flower garden to the grove and tried to pick a ripe peach, all in vain. Betsy found an unwonted charm in everything because she was showing the Briars to someone so interested, and that person none other than the Honorable George.

He tossed an orange in the air and as he caught it said suddenly, "It seems a long time since the ball." She nodded and felt a delicious little quiver run through her. "But, thank the stars, there is to be another one. Our good Colonel Bingham gives it—out of doors under a marquee. You will be there, of course. You must be. The invitations will be issued soon."

Again this tall officer, so adequate for dangerous tasks, sent her a glance of appeal. Just as he had that night at the Castle—as if she had the power to affect his happiness! It was intoxicating. Shyly she replied that she hoped her father would permit her going and they moved toward the garden gate.

"What is that building there on the knoll?" he asked with an eager note in his voice. "Let us walk up and take a look."

"No, no!" She laid a swift hand on his arm. "I couldn't bear it. I haven't been near since he left."

"He? Who?" He stared first at her, then at the pavilion. "Ah, so that is where Bonaparte stayed! I see, Miss Betsy. I do not blame you. It must have been uncommonly trying to be so close to the damned Corsican. And that pack of Frenchmen forever complaining! But now your worries are over; the sentries are gone from your gate, and there is nothing to spoil the Briars for you any longer. Oh, upon my word!" he exclaimed without a glance at the protest in her face, "my orderly has brought my horse around. It must be time to go. I cannot be late for mess."

With that he placed her hand on his arm and set off for the house at such speed that she had no chance for a word. Before he mounted his horse, however, and after he had made his farewells to the others, he managed to whisper, bowing over her hand, "We are to meet at the Governor's day after tomorrow. Miss Wilks invites us to Plantation House."

Recalling his ardent look, Betsy no longer dreaded her own dreams. For now she had only to think of the Ensign and a strange, tingling bliss descended upon her. Every morning she awoke with the feeling that there was a very special reason for being alive—a reason in uniform. Indeed, joy so wrapped her about these days that even her sister's teasing failed to annoy her.

It was after the tea party at Plantation House that Jane took this line. She began it in the presence of Dr. O'Meara who had ridden over from Longwood one day. "Doctor," said she, with laughing eyes, "those two walked for a whole hour in the periwinkle garden, leaving all the other guests. And by the time they came back the Honorable George was calling my sister Betsy. What on earth were you talking about all the time?"

Betsy looked dreamy. "Oh, it was he who was talking —about his home. He said if he were there this December he could be skating and driving in sleighs. And he talked of his hero, the Duke of Wellington."

Dr. O'Meara said in a slightly ironic tone, "As a soldier young Carestairs would be obliged to admire the peerless general. But he doubtless regrets the Irish ancestry of Wellington. I happen to know that the Carestairs are a great Tory family. They would find it difficult to

[137]

like anyone who is not English. I pity a Frenchman who strayed upon their estate."

"Then he probably loathes Boney," commented Jane. "It seems odd with your ideas, Betsy, that you do not find Oliver Fehrzen more attractive. You danced with the Major at the ball, but have never mentioned him since. I find him very liberal. He told me he had made Sir George Cockburn promise to present him to General Bonaparte. I think Major Fehrzen would like you to talk to him about Boney, and indeed shows every sign of wanting some share of your favor."

"Surely not, if he has yours," retorted Betsy. Whereupon the two others, amused at her repartee, assured her she was becoming very much a woman of the world.

How impossible, thought the girl, that anyone could be preferred to George Carestairs. It was too bad he was prejudiced against Boney, but perhaps that was only because he did not know him. The thought made her realize afresh how dreadfully she had missed that wonderful presence. She could hardly wait until Thursday brought around the anticipated trip to Longwood. If only he had not changed in the meantime!

Her first impression on the day of their visit was that Napoleon had not altered in the least. He entered the Longwood drawing-room with the same warm cordiality, the same affectionate teasing. But when they sat down to luncheon he seemed more preoccupied and grave than he had ever been. Inasmuch as the burden of talk was thrown upon Las Cases, it was well that the latter made every effort to be agreeable. Gourgaud, on the other hand, was stiff and aloof. Betsy was sure something had offended him again or made him jealous of the Chamberlain.

After luncheon, however, the Balcombes' host grew more lively. He showed them all about the house. They praised it as best they could, but the rooms were small and dark, and the few pieces of Empire furniture made all the other chairs and tables look like dingy sticks. Only the billiard room had proportions of any space. The girls lingered there examining the maps on the walls after their father, who had business in Jamestown, had taken his leave.

"Come, Mademoiselle Betsee, I shall teach you how to play this game," said Napoleon cheerfully. And he seemed highly amused when her vicious lunge with the cue sent a ball thumping against his hand. He put it to his lips to blow the hurt away and cried between the cracks of his fingers, "Ah, will you never grow up, naughty one? You learn nothing from being pursued by a handsome cavalier, nothing from attending balls and teas!" Then, as she blushed deeply and hung her head, wondering who could have brought him gossip, he burst into jolly laughter.

Betsy's spirits rose to hear. Softly pinching Jane's arm as a signal not to interfere, she said, "Monsieur le Général, this room would be quite large enough for dancing. When are you going to give the ball you were always promising me? You never kept that promise at the Briars, but now you could do so and you must!"

Napoleon chuckled and said it was impossible. Whereupon she upraided him further for faithlessness. After they had exchanged a number of friendly insults, he said,

"I am far too busy with my memoirs to stop for a ball. But I will pay a forfeit for my broken promise. What do you choose for compensation?"

The answer was instantaneous. "A game of Blind Man's Buff."

Jane looked horrified. But Napoleon went at once to the bell rope in the corner of the room and summoned a servant. He ordered the chairs carried out of the room and sent for Emanuel Las Cases. When the page arrived he brought with him little Napoleon Bertrand, a charming boy of seven who kissed Betsy's hand with the air of a courtier. Gourgaud also strolled into the room, hands in his breeches pockets, head disdainfully high.

But Napoleon's spirits were higher. He commanded that everybody draw lots for the role of Blind Man and requested Gourgaud to tear up slips of paper and write on one "La Mort." Whoever drew that slip must be blindfolded. With a gleam of mischief in his eyes Napoleon himself passed the basket of names. The boys snatched their slips, took a fearful look and shouted gleefully, "Not I." Jane and Gourgaud followed suit. Betsy drew and saw it was marked "Death."

"You arranged it so! You cheated. It isn't fair," she cried.

But her protest was in vain. Her eyes were bound with a silk handkerchief and over this Napoleon tied one from his own pocket. "Voilà, leetle monkey. You cannot see now."

So the chase began. Betsy could soon have caught one of the boys as he darted past, or Gourgaud, who was slow. But she wanted larger game. Stumbling about she more than once felt Napoleon tap her cheek, but he always managed to dart away. At last her arms went around a figure and she felt in her own those unmistakable, plump, soft hands. "I have got you! I have got you," she cried, tearing at her bandage. "Now you shall be blindfolded."

A burst of laughter answered. Her freed vision then beheld her sister standing captive. Over Jane's shoulder Napoleon had merely stretched his hands to fool her. "Oh, how terrible you are, monsieur!" she raged. "But you shall be the Blind Man all the same."

She was after him in a rush, but he nimbly darted away. As Napoleon dodged about the billiard table, eluding capture, the room rang with shouts of mirth from the onlookers. Suddenly the door of the billiard room was flung wide open by a lackey. There stood Count Bertrand, his jaw dropping in amazement, and behind him were two men in uniform.

"Forgive me, your Majesty," stammered the Grand Marshal into the hush fallen upon the topsy-turvy room. "I had no idea. Marchand gave me no warning. We shall await your pleasure in the drawing-room."

The door closed. But Betsy had been very near it. Over the Frenchman's shoulder she had recognized the visitors. One of them was Sir George Cockburn and the other— she could scarcely believe her eyes—was Ensign Carestairs. In that split second his glance had flung at her a vitriolic compound of surprise and outrage.

8

"PROMISE YOU WILL NEVER SEE HIM AGAIN!"

Betsy stood transfixed. He *did* hate Boney. And he despised her for being on intimate, playful footing with the "Enemy." What a terrible look! Her body seemed to sink down into a dark pit, leaving her behind, numbed and sick.

With a dulled eye she observed that Napoleon, as if he cared nothing for his dignity, was quite unperturbed. He calmly pulled the bell rope, said something to the servant who appeared, something else to Gourgaud, and then strode across the room. He was taking leave of Jane and of her. Would they come again soon—very soon? They must report to him all about Colonel Bingham's ball. His smile flashed over them, neither merry nor teasing, but unexpectedly sweet. Young Emanuel Las Cases sprang to open the door for him and he was gone.

As she and her sister mounted their horses a few moments later, Betsy looked about her wanly. Everything was in keeping with her mood. Forlorn, forlorn! A fine rain was falling and the ground about the stone house was nothing but trampled mud. Dark and frowning were the iron-clad hills beyond the dreary plain. At the Guard House where a sentry marched grimly to and fro, she looked back in time to see Gourgaud coming around the house. She was about to lift her whip in a gesture of farewell, but checked the movement. From his face, also, was leveled upon her that same jet-black of disgust.

With feet hushed on the wet road which wound about the misty peaks, the two horses trotted rhythmically. Now in the silence the girl could look upon the weight within her heart and ask why it came there. She was only having a little fun to liven things up. Yet Bertrand had been horrified, the Admiral contemptuous. Gourgaud, who had liked the fun as much as she, was sour with shame for having joined it. They didn't matter much. What hurt was that Carestairs had been so revolted. It would be dreadful now to meet him at Sir George Bingham's ball. She wished she could become ill.

Nothing saved her from that party, however. But when she descended from the Wilks' carriage behind her sister she was almost glad. In the brightness of early evening the scene looked entrancing. She would never have guessed that any part of the camp at Deadwood could have been so tricked out. Between the awning over the refreshment tables and the mammoth marquee stretched above the dancing floor, lanterns were strung on ropes. Already the band was playing *The World Turned Upside Down*. Colorful uniforms and light frocks wove a pattern in and about the tents. Gay voices called greetings. And here was Major Fehrzen, begging for a dance before she could even remove her cashmere shawl.

This second ball was a milestone in Betsy's feminine education. Because of her sad heart, she had no wild spirits to control. To hide its shadow she used her own instinctive wiles and copied others she had noted. Proof of their worth was the unceasing clamor of partners for her hand. Jane, enormously engaged herself, smiled approval upon her now and then. Since Mrs. Balcombe was ill, the girls were under the official wing of the Governor's lady. But that was a wing much occupied in flight. Mrs. Wilks, a beautiful dancer and lovely besides, was almost as much in demand as her stepdaughter, the charming Laura. So Betsy's whirl was hampered only by her sharp sense of a missing presence.

It was very late and she had been dancing for hours when she suddenly turned to meet the eyes of George Carestairs. How long he had been watching her she never knew. But something fixed in his stare told her it had been for no brief time. The instant their glances crossed he joined the laughing group about her and with easy diplomacy led her away. She longed to resist his mightiness, but the stars seemed all at once to be singing in the sky and she could not. When he seated himself beside her in an obscure corner of the refreshment tent, however, and looked squarely down, the song ceased.

"You have advanced in years, Betsy, since I caught my last glimpse of you," began the Ensign superbly. Disregarding the flush brought to her cheek by the sting of his tone, he went on, "Since that revelation, I made inquiries about the events at the Briars in which you were concerned and what I was told has shocked me deeply."

Had anyone else said this, Betsy would have laughed.

But her humor had fled. Before the mirror of his face she tried on an expression of disdain, but feared it was rather crooked. "Indeed!" she said. But she wished, since she was to be scolded like a child, that she might act the part—scratch and kick or burst into tears.

"They say you and this fat little Corsican are friends— close friends! I cannot comprehend such a thing. My family always considered Bonaparte a low scoundrel." He glared his contempt. "Don't you know this fine playmate of yours is a monster of ambition who stopped at nothing? How can a girl like you tolerate such a being? Perhaps you would like him to get free and shed more of your countrymen's blood!"

"Stop!" she cried. "I don't care what you think! It's you who do not understand!"

She tried to rise, but a strong hand held her fast. Asked to explain then, she was silent. How could she express her complicated feelings? She herself had never got them clear. With eyes looking straight ahead she still could sense how compelling in its scorn and anger was the Ensign's clean-cut face.

"I have never been so mistaken in anyone," he murmured. "I thought you were loyal and had taste. I thought we felt alike. It makes me heartsick."

At that moment through the other opening of the tent a laughing group entered and stood about the punch table. Betsy saw a tall woman in a geranium brocade wave a hand toward her and recognized Madame Bertrand.

"Betsy, do affairs go well?" she called out in French

with laughter in her voice. "You and Jane must come soon to call. We are settled at Huts Gate now."

The girl managed to smile and return the greeting. But she felt the curious eyes of the others focusing upon her and her companion and, taking advantage of their presence, she got to her feet. As she walked out into the air, however, it was with her hand tightly imprisoned in the crook of the Ensign's arm.

Suddenly an inspiration came to her—a speech once heard in amateur theatricals. With her chin up she repeated the heroine's words, "Please leave me. You have had your say. Now go!"

In spite of her rage and fear that Carestairs would literally vanish forever from her sight, some part of her enjoyed that bit of drama. Still more she liked its effect.

"Betsy!" cried the Honorable George in quite another tone. "Can't you see that feeling as I do about you, I can't bear your having aught to do with that man? I never dreamed— Why, Sir George told me you wept to have Bonaparte leave the Briars. Oh, promise you will never see him again. I have been on the battlefield against his troops. I hate him for what his thirst for power has cost."

"But, George—" she questioned slowly, "since you don't hate war, can't you at least admit Boney is a great general? A man of genius?"

"God save us, no. I took good care to avoid conversation with him on shipboard—the low-born tyrant! As for the other day at Longwood, the Admiral had merely bade me escort him in place of his orderly. Once presented, I clicked my heels and retired outside. Genius? That up-start? Bah!"

With all her heart Betsy longed to drop the argument. It was hateful to quarrel when they could be talking hap-pily as before. Yet something stronger than her will cried out in her voice, "Can you deny that it took all the armies of Europe to beat him? Didn't he win power in the first place by ability alone? He's not an upstart. All his people wanted him for Emperor. You are not fair!"

She saw surprise creep into the haughty face. After a pause he said, "You defend him, eh? You won't accept what I say?" Yet he spoke as if the bubble of his violence had been pricked.

Quickly she hurried to press the advantage. "You really don't know him, George. I used to think of him as an ogre, too. But I found he can be charming and he is brave about his fate. Could you not believe that the Emperor you hate is one thing and the Boney I like is another? I've seen him every day, listened to his wonderful talk. He's been my neighbor. It makes a difference." She added wistfully, "We had such jolly times together."

They had been strolling over the uneven ground and some time since had paused within the shadow of a clump of scrub pines. Betsy felt her shoulders clutched by two imperious hands. Stern was the face bent down upon her.

"Why do you set yourself against me? It's treachery to be friends with him, I tell you! If you are too young to understand that, then—Betsy, this is very serious, very important—how can you understand the way I've come to regard you? Yet I thought you did."

With these words the girl's heart sprang upward once

[147]

more. In spite of everything, he did care about her! Wasn't that all that mattered? She looked up, tremulously happy again, the question in her eyes.

Just then voices sounded near them. They heard the band striking up. A pair of officers approached across the parade ground. As Carestairs' hands fell to his sides and they both moved out of the shadow, a slim figure in uniform rushed from the marquee and bounded toward them. "Miss Betsy Balcombe is wanted," called the orderly. "This is her quadrille with Colonel Bingham."

After that dance Mrs. Wilks ordered her carriage. As the three young ladies were gathering around her, Baron Gourgaud rushed up to say farewell to Miss Laura. With a fiery look of devotion he carried her hand to his lips. But Betsy saw only pity and regret in the charming facè bent over him. Oh, how differently she herself would reward such a gesture from George Carestairs. She looked wildly about for a last glimpse of him, but in vain.

What he had said that night, however, worked in her veins like a powerful potion. Was he right or was he prejudiced? She could not decide. The question was part of the conflict which seemed to possess everyone at St. Helena. In the next few weeks the girl had Napoleon almost more vividly before her than when he was at the Briars in the flesh. Talk about him never stopped. Nobody dropped in without comment or news or gossip concerning the French colony and its dominating figure. And weary as she grew of the discussion, Betsy was forever impelled to listen.

The very day after the dance her father started this ball rolling. Although she had been half dozing on the piazza near the drawing-room window, she was aware that inside her mother and father were conversing together. Suddenly she was aroused by a different accent in his tones.

"My dear, Longwood today was at sixes and sevens," she heard him say. "Count Bertrand is deeply offended because Boney has put Montholon in charge of the household. So to pacify him Boney rode over to Huts Gate this morning to invite the Bertrands to dinner. But, as bad luck would have it, he was stopped on the way by a sentry."

"Why?" asked Mrs. Balcombe's surprised voice. "Don't tell me General Bonaparte is not allowed to ride!"

"Well, you see, Admiral Cockburn has drawn definite limits—a circle of about twelve miles around the Longwood and Deadwood plains—within which the General and his staff can ride unattended. Outside these boundaries they have to have the escort of a British officer."

At this Betsy sprang up and bounced into the drawing-room. "That's what Boney hates most of all," she cried. "It is so humiliating to him—having a guard."

Looking anything but cordial toward this intruder, Mr. Balcombe pointedly addressed the rest of his tale to his wife. "The trouble today was that the sentry was mistaken. He should not have stopped the riders. When General Bonaparte returned to Longwood he sent Gourgaud out to ride all around the limits and ascertain their extent. Gourgaud found they could ride considerably farther than Huts Gate—beyond Miss Mason's house. So you may imagine the protest which was sent to Colonel

Bingham about being halted. Certainly this time there is undeniable reason for complaint."

"Dear me," sighed his wife, picking up again the knitting she had dropped to listen. "It is all very sad, very unpleasant. But, as you once told poor Huff, Mr. Balcombe, one must be so careful not to take sides. The Admiral is acting under orders from London and that's all there is to it."

Betsy had retreated beneath her father's frown to kneel on a chair near the door. Now she piped up irrepressibly, "But, mother, it's getting to the point where everybody who likes Boney might be accused of taking sides. Major Fehrzen was telling me last night about dining with Napoleon the first week he was up at Longwood. The Major was exceedingly well impressed with his—what did he call it?—his *benignity* and his cleverness. He admired him very much. But he said he would not dare say much about it 'in official circles.' Heavens on earth, I'm glad I'm not in official circles."

Mrs. Balcombe laughed dryly. "But that's just where you are, Betsy, as the daughter of the General Purveyor. So kindly remember that. The less you say, the better. And please do not use such strong expressions. It is not ladylike."

At this reproof Betsy made a curtsey and left the room immediately, which was perhaps just what her mother really hoped she would do. The moment she reached the garden, however, she wished she had waited to ask her father how Colonel Bingham would set right the mistake made by the sentry. Then she forgot the matter entirely. For Frank and Alex wanted her to play battledore and shuttlecock on the lawn and there were dinner guests in the evening. After that she thought only of ways to dazzle, humiliate and get the better of Ensign Carestairs.

The next afternoon, however, when she was doing an errand for her mother at Mr. Solomon's General Store, she saw General Gourgaud and Major Fehrzen dismount outside. In surprise she asked herself, "Have those two become friends?"—then realized that Gourgaud was required to have a British officer accompany him to the village. Instantly she remembered the story her father told and determined to find out its sequel. Quickly taking her change she stepped out on the Marino.

Major Fehrzen had tactfully disappeared. But Gourgaud, on the doorstep, gave her an affable greeting and seemed willing to chat. After inquiring for Napoleon's health Betsy said she had heard about the affront offered him.

"Affront?" repeated the Frenchman with a startled expression. Then he pursed his lips and nodded, "Ah, you mean his being halted on the Huts Gate road? But no, mademoiselle, that was no affront—only a mistake. Colonel Bingham came to see us and made a handsome apology. It is a horrible restriction, naturally, to have to be accompanied everywhere outside the Longwood limits. But, after all," he shrugged, "one must submit."

A few days after this encounter Betsy went for a long ride all alone. She wanted to work off her restless unhappiness. For every day she expected some word from George Carestairs and still he made no sign. Had he really ceased to care whether he saw her or not?

As she approached within a mile or two of Longwood,

she saw Miss Polly Mason standing in her garden. Betsy pulled up to a stop, expecting merely to pass the time of day. But immediately the all-absorbing topic was flung at her over the garden wall.

"Betsy," said Miss Mason, "your father must be hard pressed to provide supplies for a household run in imperial style. Every time I go toward town I pass a procession of barrels, boxes and packages on its way to Longwood."

"Yes, it's a large household," replied the girl, "but father says the special luxuries are bought by Napoleon out of his own pocket."

Miss Mason sniffed. "I expect many of them go to the cottage at Huts Gate. I went to call on Madame Bertrand yesterday. Her children are quite lovely and her husband seems devoted, but she has such a very unhappy air. I can't see why. The cottage is pleasant and what with Sunday dining at the table of her adored 'Emperor' and lunching with Admiral Cockburn, she appears to have many diversions."

Betsy stroked Tom between the ears with her riding whip. She sought for a helpful explanation. "Perhaps Madame remembers too much," she said at last. "When the Count was Governor of Illyria they lived like princes. Madame Bertrand entertained, I have been told, in a marvelous way. And then their life at the palace where her husband was Grand Marshal! After all that, Huts Gate may seem dull and small."

Miss Mason's face flushed. "No doubt we all seem dull to the Countess," she snapped. "But, as the prophet says, 'Pride goeth before a fall.' I hear this fine lady has taken a fancy to you, Betsy, but I should not see too much of her—that is my advice."

In amazement the girl saw a stiff, straight back rapidly receding through the massed sweetness of the rose garden. What had she said to provoke the woman? Vexed and mystified she touched her pony with the whip and set off at a mad gallop. Then and there she decided that most adults were both disappointing and incalculable. When she found on return home an invitation to spend the next day at the beach on Turks Cap Bay with Basil Porteous, Rose Legg and several other friends, she promptly accepted it.

It was a relief on that occasion to substitute action for talk. But the respite was short. She had ridden back with Basil to Jamestown and in front of the Porteous house she met Dr. Warden just starting up the Longwood road. He leaned from his saddle to speak to her.

"General Gourgaud is dangerously ill," he said in a low tone. "I am having a bad time with him, for he is very despondent and refuses all medicine." Then, as if the girl's dazed response had seemed to him too casual, the doctor added emphatically, "I assure you that if he doesn't yield, nothing can save him."

Through the blistering sun Betsy stared after the rider. Did anyone—even a doctor—ever get used to the idea of death, ever see it strike down a familiar person without a sense of hanging helpless over a black whirlpool? She couldn't help thinking, nevertheless, that if one had to perish, it would be nice to die of unrequited love. Without a doubt that was what was the matter with Gourgaud. Betsy wondered whether she were too healthy to manage

it. She might try, were she sure Ensign Carestairs would
be inconsolable. As she rode slowly homeward, however,
her thoughts turned to Napoleon. What a household for
him—gloom inside and out! No one to make him laugh,
as she used to do!

When Dr. Warden stopped at the Briars a few days
later, she ran down the driveway to meet him and ask for
news. The report he gave brought her a curious glow.
It seemed that the day before when the physician was
there laboring in vain with the sick man, Napoleon strode
into the room and walked straight to the bed.

"I shall always remember what General Bonaparte
said," declared Dr. Warden, "for at that moment I could
see him making his rounds after a battle, encouraging his
men, and visiting the wounded. 'What ridiculous be-
havior is this?' said the General to my patient. 'How often
have you faced Death in the field of battle without the
least sensation of fear; and now you are resolved to yield
to his power as if you were afraid to resist him. What
childish obstinacy! Play the fool no longer, I beg you,
but submit with cheerfulness to the remedies which alone
can promote your restoration to health.'"

Dr. Warden dismounted from his horse. Giving the
bridle to a small black boy who had sprung up from the
shade near the house, he continued, "I assure you, Miss
Betsy, that the reproof worked marvels. Gourgaud began
taking his medicine at once and today I find him quite
out of danger and on the road to recovery. I am the more
grateful for General Bonaparte's aid because he is rather
skeptical of the physician's power. He is an extraordinary
person." The doctor broke off with a laugh. "Really, Miss

[154]

Betsy, your expression is such that I would give as much as a shilling for your thoughts."

Betsy blushed, skipped into the house and summoned her mother to receive the visitor. She would not have told her wish for any money. But how terribly she did long to have George Carestairs hear the doctor tell that story in just that way. Surely he would not call Dr. Warden a traitor for his admiration.

That picture of Napoleon aroused her ardent wish to see him again. When she found her father alone in the study in the evening she asked him if he would arrange another visit.

"You will have to wait a bit," he replied. "Boney has shut himself up and will neither go for a ride nor receive anyone."

Betsy opened wide eyes. "Why in the world?" she asked.

Then she heard the surprising revelation Dr. Warden had made before his departure. He reported that through Count Montholon, Napoleon had sent an insulting letter to Admiral Cockburn full of all sorts of demands for more liberty. The Admiral had written a stern reply conceding nothing and Napoleon was in a black mood. "What do you think of that?" concluded her father with a probing glance.

The girl dropped her eyes to the desk and thoughtfully traced a pattern on it with a brass paper cutter. "I don't know," she murmured. "It seems petty and unreasonable on Boney's part. And yet—well, I understand that he can't forgive his title being refused. Neither can he get over being treated as if he had been captured on the battlefield instead of coming of his own free will to ask for protection from England."

"That last grudge is just play-acting," said William Balcombe. "The fact is General Bonaparte could do nothing else. Since he could not get to America, the jig was up. Russia and Germany would have torn him in pieces. France under the Bourbons would have had him shot. He had to surrender. All the same, he ought not to be pestered with pettiness. Alas, child," he patted Betsy's shining hair, "it is a hard position for those of us who see both sides of the case."

Betsy shot her father a grateful look. How comforting to know that he, too, sympathized with Boney. Then slowly she repeated his phrase, *"Both* sides?"

Mr. Balcombe chuckled. Turning back to his papers, he said, "Yes, Betsy, the English officials deserve a bit of sympathy themselves. They have plenty of difficulties. Don't forget that."

Before the week was out Betsy recalled her father's remark under dramatic circumstances. They occurred at a luncheon the Balcombes gave for Admiral Cockburn. Betsy was allowed to skip lessons in order to arrange flowers and help with preparations. As she saw the brilliant uniforms assembling on the lawn, she thought it was quite like those marvelous days when Boney lived at the Briars.

She had been warned to remain in the background. But hardly had Admiral Cockburn greeted his hostess when he asked in his hearty voice, "Where is Miss Betsy? I have something for her."

The girl stepped forward with face alight with curiosity. In exchange for her deep curtsey the guest of honor gave her a small box tied with a purple ribbon. Lowering his tone almost to a whisper, Sir George said, "This token comes from a certain Ensign whom we keep too busy for gallantry. After his turn in the boats at night, he must sleep by day. Other times he is too much occupied to arrange for the special pass he needs to get about in the evening. A sad case, indeed!" The Admiral chuckled heartlessly. "But young Carestairs manages to think of you all the same, miss. So do not be insensible to him!"

Insensible? The eminent messenger never knew how narrowly he escaped being hugged for his pains. The girl slipped away and behind a clump of pepper trees undid the ribbon. Inside the box lay a paper scrawled in a bold hand, "For Betsy." Beneath it lay a little gold locket set with a queer green stone. George! She clasped the chain around her throat with glad fingers. She would wear it every moment, day and night—a pledge!

In high spirits she took her place at the long luncheon table. Airily she practiced flirting with young Major Fehrzen on her right and made the shy middle-aged officer on her left talk to her about his campaigns. Yet she cocked an ear when the Admiral boomed out to Mrs. Balcombe, "Captain Poppleton regretted his inability to accept your hospitality, ma'm. But General Bonaparte goes for a long ride this noon and he had to attend him."

Betsy was glad to hear it. Boney always felt better after exercise. Idly she wondered in what direction he had ridden. What was her amazement, therefore, just as the strawberries and champagne had been served, to see appear in the doorway Captain Poppleton's face distorted by emotion. Pushing past a servant, the officer entered the room and his voice drowned all laughter and talk about the table.

"Admiral Cockburn, I have lost the Emperor!"

Heads turned, chairs were pushed back, exclamations went off like small torpedoes. Every glance fled from the panting Poppleton to the guest of honor. For an instant Sir George stared, wine glass halfway to his lips. Then he set it down steadily and in the tense silence said calmly, "Nonsense, Captain! What happened?"

"We started down the road beyond Miss Mason's, sir. I was at the usual distance in the rear. Then Count Bertrand turned back and declared I was approaching 'His Majesty' too closely and asked me to withdraw still farther. This I did to oblige them. At once Bonaparte, Gourgaud and Bertrand spurred their horses into a gallop, dived up a steep side path and disappeared. Search as I would, I could find no trace of them. I rode almost to Sandy Bay and back."

The Admiral's brow darkened and he choked back some violent comment. Finally he said in a tone of quiet authority, "Return to Longwood, Captain Poppleton. You will find General Bonaparte there at luncheon. Put up the signal flag to telegraph me confirmation."

With a look of unutterable relief, Poppleton clicked his heels, bowed and left the room. It was already humming with talk. Although the Admiral loudly resumed his description of the fine vegetable garden he was making in a corner of Deadwood, nobody listened. Betsy heard the officer next her growl in fury, "That's the way the

damned Corsican proves himself worthy of more liberty
and further concessions!"

To herself Betsy said, "It is only Boney's mischief—
just like his stealing my ball dress!" Yet she knew it was
a vexing form of joke and, meeting her father's eyes, she
bit her lip and nodded. He was right. The British officials
had their trials, indeed.

Betsy was not surprised to hear next day that Captain
Poppleton had been unmercifully teased by a gleeful run-
away when he returned to Longwood. According to
Major Fehrzen, the luckless officer was equally harassed
by his fellows. Whenever Poppleton appeared at mess, a
shout would go up, "He's lost the Emperor!" Throughout the island, however, Napoleon was seriously criti-
cized for his escapade. People declared he had tricked his
escort in order to reconnoiter a place of escape. They
spoke of Elba, shook their heads, and said extra guards
were needed at Longwood.

While talk of the incident was still seething, a mail
boat arrived from England. Journals and reviews featur-
ing pieces written shortly after Waterloo sounded a note
which chimed completely with the general nervousness.
One afternoon Betsy picked up the *Quarterly Review*
for October, 1815. In the midst of a savage article which
declared that "Bonaparte should have been brought to the
block," she found this paragraph:

The custody of Bonaparte which Europe has confided
to us is a very ticklish point and do as we may we shall
hardly escape censure; if he be not actually confined, he

[159]

may and probably will escape; if he be confined, we shall have all the Oppositions in Europe crying shame.

With her finger in the page, she rose to greet Dr. O'Meara who had been talking with her father in the study. At his request she showed him what she had been reading. He glanced the paragraph through, then lifted his head with a jerk.

"Well, God save us," he blurted out angrily, "isn't he confined on this terrible rock in the most desolate spot of all? He is almost blown away by winds and rain. What does the government want—a dungeon? Bah, all this gossip here about General Bonaparte's planning to escape is utter nonsense. He couldn't if he would and he wouldn't if he could! More likely he'll meet an early death for lack of sufficient free exercise. Then all the damned ministers will congratulate themselves."

Waving his arms over his head, the doctor stamped off to get his horse. Betsy looked after him thoughtfully. Here, indeed, was a sympathizer. The tempery Irishman, always opposed to the British Government, reminded her a little of Mr. Huff. Although she agreed about Boney's not wishing to escape, she was glad she didn't hate England in such a fashion. Fingering her locket, she wafted a message to Deadwood, "George, please understand! I only want to be fair."

That same evening after dinner Mr. Balcombe announced to his daughters a piece of news he and Mrs. Balcombe had known for some time. The Wilks were soon to leave the island and another Governor, Sir Hudson Lowe, was to take his place. The two girls were loud

in their laments. What, they asked, would St. Helena do without the kind, hospitable Wilks, so beloved by everybody? Betsy thought of poor Gourgaud's sorrow. Jane speculated about the new administrator.

In the midst of the talk a messenger introduced a happier theme. Madame Bertrand had sent an invitation to the Misses Balcombe to come to luncheon and stay until the moon was up. She also promised a glimpse of "The Emperor" who had been inquiring for them.

On the appointed day the pair set gaily off. As they mounted their ponies, Betsy said with an innocent air, "Let's go by way of Jamestown. I need a skein of silk to finish the embroidery on my new neck ruffle."

Unsuspectingly Jane agreed. So the younger girl got what she had been hoping chance might grant. It was not the silk yarn, for this she could not match. But on the road past Deadwood they met three horsemen. Even at a distance Betsy recognized each one and felt as if she might fall from her saddle with joy.

"Here comes Colonel Bingham!" cried Jane and pulled up for a greeting.

Betsy reined in Tom. She also bowed and smiled as the Colonel and Major Fehrzen doffed their hats. But it was toward the Colonel's other escort that her eyes fled hungrily. Not in all these long weeks had she had a glimpse of Ensign Carestairs. Nor had he replied to her note of thanks for the locket. But now as their glances met, the marvelous sense of something humming wordlessly between them told her that it was not indifference which had kept him away.

Major Fehrzen broke that bewitched communion.

"Catch, Miss Betsy!" Gaily he tossed a fat rosebud into her lap. "A pretty farmer's lass gave it me this morning. What's her name? The one they call The Nymph of the Valley."

She sniffed the rose and murmured a reply. In desperation she saw Colonel Bingham gather up his reins again. They musn't go yet! "Colonel Bingham!" she cried, "father says he is going to give me a ball on my birthday. Will you come? Will you promise to give your officers leave to attend?"

"All my officers?" Sir George looked at her with friendly irony.

"Well, at least, those now present and a dozen others who like dancing!" She knew she was blushing, but flicked a glance at the Honorable George and found him smiling delightedly.

"I shall try my best, Miss Betsy. Thank you. Send me word as to the day."

Already he was moving onward. Major Fehrzen, with a gallant wave of his hat, swept after, calling out his good-bys. The last rider, however, brought his horse close to Betsy. His hand was on his heart and he looked into her eyes as if he were casting himself into a well. What was he saying? He had passed before she knew. But when he looked back, she was gazing after him with a stricken face. Like an automaton, she followed Jane with that request ringing in her ears: "Don't go to Longwood today, Betsy!" he had said. "Pray don't go! You won't, if you care!"

Madame Bertrand's whitewashed cottage, tucked into a small garden amid tall pines, was charming. Both the children and their mother warmly welcomed the two girls, showed them about and pointed out the grandeur of the view over the strange valley. Yet, despite all her efforts Betsy's inner turmoil was observed.

Handing her a glass of wine, Madame Bertrand said, "Drink this, my dear. You look pale. It is hot for riding, I know, or perhaps you have been doing too much. How is the haughty young Ensign whom you captured with one smile?"

Jane answered carelessly, "We just met Mr. Carestairs on the road with Colonel Bingham. Sir George says the new Governor is expected any day now. Do you know him, Madame?"

Betsy sipped her wine in heavy-hearted silence. She couldn't refuse to see Boney for the sake of George! It was impossible. Aside from discourtesy to her hostess, she herself desired greatly to go to Longwood. Yet, if George heard of it, after what he had said, it might be the end— the very end of everything between them. How queer that she could care this way when it made her so unhappy. She felt as if she had swallowed lead. Suddenly Jane's eyes warned her that she must rouse herself to talk.

After luncheon came the moment of decision. The walk over to Longwood was proposed and Madame Bertrand looked expectantly at Betsy. For an instant, feeling herself at a crossroads, she hesitated.

"The Emperor misses you, I think, Betsy," said Madame Bertrand. "He speaks of you as his dear Imp, his sunshine friend. You must have made him forget that he has nothing very real with which to occupy his energy."

His friend! Betsy could waver no longer. As the three women reached the garden gate, little Napoleon Bertrand ran up to Betsy. Fixing upon her eyes luminous with envy, he said, "Mademoiselle, is it that you will play Blind Man's Buff with the Emperor today?"

Faintly smiling, she said no and realized with a start how few weeks had elapsed since that game had made the terrible rift between her and George.

At the lodge gate, Madame Bertrand handed a paper to the sentry. She murmured to the girls, "Doubtless the Grand Marshal's wife and her guests would be allowed to enter unchallenged. But I thought best to have my husband sign this pass. Nobody, you understand, but the inhabitants of Longwood is permitted inside the gate without one."

Betsy thought ruefully of the days when she could rush up the path to greet Boney at almost any hour. Such informality seemed even more remote as Marchand announced them. After an impressive instant of waiting, the footman opened the doors of the drawing-room and Napoleon came forward to greet them, his hat under his arm.

It was startling to observe how he and Madame Bertrand measured one another in a glance of veiled hostility. "She is his public champion and his private foe." As the phrase sprang into Betsy's mind, she remembered the tale of Madame's attempt to jump into the sea rather than come to St. Helena and felt moved by pity and admiration for her self-control.

"We are going driving with my new horses from the Cape," said Napoleon after the greetings were over. "Will that not please you, Betsee?" He smiled and pinched her cheek.

The girl drew back. "Oh, non, monsieur le Général! I am terrified of driving on these roads. Please let us stay and talk or else walk out toward the wood. Do not make us drive!"

At once the warm companion changed into the man whose will was law. Annoyance hardened the gray eyes. "Bah! You must not be a little poltroon. Certainly we are going. My man Archambaud has the carriage ready now."

He strode away toward the rear door of the house and there was nothing to do but follow. On the driver's box Archambaud grinned and touched his hat. Two plump gray steeds snorted and pawed the earth in the leather traces fastened to the light carriage. Betsy and Jane were commanded to sit opposite Napoleon and Madame Bertrand beside him. The instant the groom sprang away from the horses' heads, they were off. Down the rough, narrow trail to the woods, the fierce little pair tore at full speed. The carriage swayed and trembled. The wheels, narrowly grazing the huge rocks at the side of the road, sent the pebbles flying.

Napoleon laughed with glee. "This is the chariot of Phoebus. But, voilà! Mees Betsee becomes pale. She is a coward."

It was worse in the woods. There the trail was lost in a welter of fallen leaves and gnarled roots. Twisting about, Betsy watched the horses rushing blindly ahead, dodging between tree trunks at the pull of Archambaud's strong hands. At every instant she expected the animals to

[165]

stumble or the carriage to crash against some obstacle. Cold sweat dampened her brow. She could scarcely keep from screaming. All the time Napoleon, between bursts of loud laughter, was shouting, "Bon! Bon! Faster! Faster! What a fine team I have."

When at last they came out on the Deadwood road, the girl turned and glanced at Madame Bertrand. She was taut as a woman of wire and her eyes were wild. Even Jane looked perturbed and indignant. What a way to treat guests, raged Betsy! At that instant she positively hated Napoleon. A cruel, inhuman tyrant—that's what he was!

Suddenly he shouted to Archambaud to stop. When the excited little steeds had finally been pulled back on their haunches and the carriage came to a standstill, Napoleon stood up and stretched out an arm.

"Look over there where those soldiers are working!" he said and pulled Betsy up beside him. "They are making an excellent vegetable garden. Every day I pass them and find the same young officer in charge. He works with a will and his men seem to like him. Here, take my glass!" He slipped from his shoulder the strap of the military glasses he always carried. "See if you know who he is. His face is slightly familiar as if I had met him—perhaps on shipboard. I like soldiers and this youth has aroused my interest."

With hands still trembling from strain, Betsy fixed the field glass to her eyes and focused on the tall figure standing at the edge of the plowed earth. "Ah!" she cried out as if in pain.

"Promise You Will Never See Him Again!"

"Do you know him? Who is he?" asked her companion.

The girl handed him his glass, sank into her seat, and said in a faint voice, "His name is the Honorable George Carestairs. He is an Ensign." To avoid Madame Bertrand's knowing glance, she turned her head away.

"Really?" said Napoleon in a warm tone. He looked again through the glass. "It is exceptional that a man of high birth should be so workmanlike and energetic. He must be a fine fellow." He sat down, took Betsy's hand and with a charming look of affection said playfully, "It is too bad he is an aristocrat, for that is the sort of man you should marry, ma petite amie, a man of true worth. If you are wise enough to choose such an one, I shall give you a beautiful wedding present. Have you met the Ensign? Do you like him?"

Gently the carriage began to move forward again. Jane leaned from her seat and said teasingly, "Monsieur, we think she has lost her heart to that young man."

"What? Is it so?" The imprisoned fingers were eagerly pressed.

A sob rose in Betsy's throat. Oh, why did they all stare so? She felt as if her secret heart had been snatched out before their curious eyes. She cried out fiercely, "No, I don't like him! He is a domineering popinjay. He abuses you!"

Hearty laughter met her words. "But certainly! That matters not in the least. It is only that he looks upon me as a terrible enemy of his country. Do not be so foolish as to quarrel with your lover about me, my child. Your happiness is the important matter, petite Betsee."

[167]

Your lover! Those words, never spoken before, never quite dreamed, rang in Betsy's memory like a chime of bells. It echoed a promise of reconciliation and understanding. As for the person who had set these words to sounding, how could she ever turn from him even when he was selfish and perverse? He had a nature spacious enough for admiration and for tolerance. Surely somehow George Carestairs would feel the generosity of this "terrible enemy" and would know that she could never give up his friendship!

PERILOUS ADVENTURE

"Have you seen the new Governor? What is he like? As nice as Colonel Wilks?"

All the Balcombes had long been waiting on the veranda for the head of the house to return with news from Jamestown. But, as usual, it was Betsy who first hurled the questions everyone wanted answered. The *Phaeton,* a frigate manned with forty-six guns, had arrived the day before with Sir Hudson and Lady Lowe, Lady Bingham, the Governor's administrative secretary, Major Gorrequer and other officers. Already everyone on St. Helena was wondering what changes would follow the new régime.

William Balcombe sat down on the edge of the veranda rail, smiled at the eager faces before him and took a pinch of snuff. "Well," he began deliberately, "let us begin with the important sex. Lady Lowe has only recently married Sir Hudson. She was a widow and is accompanied by the daughter of that union, Miss Charlotte Johnson—a bit older than you, Betsy. Lady Bingham seems an aristocrat to her finger-tips. Her husband, by the way, has been promoted. He is Brigadier-General now."

"But the Governor!" cried Mrs. Balcombe impatiently. "Do get on to him, my dear."

"Yes, yes. Sir Hudson Lowe brings with him a reputation for excellent service. Yet—his looks are not impressive—rather sparse red hair and a straight, thin mouth. Not an appealing personality compared to Colonel Wilks. I should imagine Sir Hudson has a temper. And I am quite certain he has high esteem for his position."

"And why not, father?" put in Jane, leaning eagerly forward. "They say Governor Lowe will receive twelve thousand pounds a year."

Her father did not answer for a moment and his eyes wandered down the valley. "I wonder," he mused, "how his first interview with General Bonaparte will come off. Admiral Cockburn is to present him at Longwood."

It was some time, however, before reports of that interview reached the Briars. In the meantime Betsy's attention was occupied with the departure of Colonel and Mrs. Wilks. Miss Laura had already sailed, leaving Baron Gourgaud and many another officer despondent. Now the Colonel and his wife were receiving farewells and the Balcombe girls planned to call on a certain Thursday afternoon.

"Major Fehrzen said he would like to go over with us," Jane announced. "I shall let him know that we must start by three o'clock."

But when the time came around Betsy ran into the house from a trip to the stables crying, "Jane, I can't go with you after all. Tom has a kind of distemper and since father and mother have the fillies, there is only one decent mount left."

Perilous Adventure

Before the hall mirror Jane was adjusting her little plumed hat. "The poor Major will be crushed," she said, turning around. Then her eyes fled far past Betsy's shoulder. "Why, look! What in the world? Who are these?"

Coming down the driveway was a horse bearing two young men in uniform who were laughing uproariously. By the time the girls reached the lawn they had dismounted. One was the expected Major and the other, George Carestairs. The latter stopped laughing the moment he saw Betsy and made it plain by one look that he had not forgiven her for going to see Napoleon.

"Miss Balcombe," Major Fehrzen was saying, "you see before you a Good Samaritan. When I met Carestairs walking up here afoot, I was moved by compassion and set him on my own beast and brought him here."

Jane laughed. "Really, Major, I think the poor beast with his double load was the Samaritan."

"Where is your father, Miss Balcombe?" asked Carestairs, pointedly addressing Jane. Learning that he was away from home, the Ensign looked troubled. "I have here an important document from the Admiral which he wished Mr. Balcombe to read while I waited. But I presume I must leave it and send an orderly for it later. Will you allow me to place it in his study?"

While the two were gone, Betsy went over to give the Major's horse a piece of sugar. She wished he were Pegasus ready to bear her off to the coast of Africa far from a handsome Ensign who disapproved of her. It was surprising to hear Major Fehrzen say in a warm, friendly tone, "I always like to watch you with animals, Miss Betsy. You have a way with them."

Her look of pleasure at his praise was deflected by the return of Carestairs with her sister. But Fehrzen recaptured her attention by proposing that they all four ride over to Plantation House. When he learned of the shortage of horses in the Balcombe stable, he said with his eyes on Betsy, "Well, let us walk! Isn't there a short passage on foot?"

"Yes," said Betsy, "but it is not much frequented. One must climb down the ravine and then over a mountain to get there. It is very wild."

"Good," returned the Major with infectious gaiety and clapped the Ensign on the back. "Come, Carestairs, you may not get leave again soon and should bid adieu to the Colonel and his lady. Lead the way, Miss Betsy."

Such was the force of his enthusiasm that somehow they all started forward. In spite of Jane's horrified protests and the Ensign's glum demeanor, they were soon at the descent above the waterfall. Betsy with no real conviction that the plan would be carried out went on without a pause. Lightly and skillfully she glided down between rocks and giant ferns. Soon she was excitedly aware that George was following closely. As she began to mount the precipitous slope ahead, however, a shout arose far behind.

"Come back!" called Jane. "Come back!" shouted the Major. "We can't do it."

Carestairs looked down at Betsy with an unwilling smile. She hooked an arm around a slim gum tree and mockingly made him a half curtsey. "It is not too steep for me, sir. Go join Jane. I have a mind to go on a bit."

Then for the first time her companion broke his silence.

Looking aghast, he cried, "What? Alone? Impossible!"

Here in this primitive wilderness the girl felt wild and free as a bird. For the moment she hardly cared whether the young man stayed or went. She swung one foot back and forth and sent him an impish look. "Oh, I have climbed this cliff more than once with Gregory Doveton. Please go and reassure Jane. She would disapprove only of our taking the walk alone together." To the baffled look of her companion she added coquettishly, "Why don't you exchange places with Major Fehrzen? I don't believe Jane would mind his accompanying me and I think he might like to do so."

At that Carestairs flushed and said quickly. "He might, indeed. The fellow admires even your being so head-strong."

Another insistent call arose from the dark tangle below. Betsy's answer was to turn a rebellious back and start up the cliff again. Whereupon her companion hurled down his decision in a mighty shout. "Hello, Major! We are going on! Meet us at Plantation House!"

Betsy acknowledged the faint protesting answer by waving a delighted hand to her fellow truant. Then she went on climbing. Occasionally her sure little foot in its impracticable black slipper lost its hold. Now and then her frock of fine cambric caught on a bramble. At such moments she would be aware of a firm arm at her waist or a quick hand ready to help. But her brief word of thanks was the only utterance between them until at last they reached the top of the height. Then Carestairs, with a look of irrepressible admiration, snatched off his hat and cried, "Well done!"

[173]

Exulting in his approval, the girl sank down panting on a bed of moss in the shadow of an enormous boulder. After a moment her companion sat down beside her. Through half-closed eyes she was aware of his wondering scrutiny.

"I have never known a young lady like you," he said slowly. "My sister and my cousins would be good for nothing more than a country ramble. They have no such freedom as yours here. It makes you—different."

Betsy, still motionless, considered the comparison. A picture from earliest childhood emerged distinct—a Sunday morning in summer when she walked over the English downs with Granny to the village church. She remembered the young ladies in a flutter of white frocks, blue ribbons and flowered bonnets, all so carefully guarded by mothers and aunts. That was the sort of girl George had known. Never before had she realized how she would hate being so proper and so sheltered—with never a chance for a wild ride alone or an expedition like this one with its spice of physical danger. Did George like her less or better for being "different"?

She opened wide eyes upon him. But he had sprung to his feet and was holding out his hand. "Come!" said he, "we must not linger here. The others, on their horses, will arrive before us."

The descent was harder than the climb. Time and again loose stones would slide from under their feet and to save themselves from falling they clung to tree branches and rocks. The sun beat down fearfully hot, but Betsy felt too happy for fatigue. Surely after this adventure George and she would never quarrel again.

They had almost reached the base of the cliff now and Carestairs was going ahead. Such was the steepness that she could often look over his shoulder down upon the half-obliterated path. Suddenly, with a cry, she flung her arms about his waist and pulled him backwards. As he half fell against a log, she stooped and flung downward with all her might a slab of rock. Scrambling to his feet with an exclamation of amazement the young man looked where her trembling finger pointed. From under the stone she had so surely aimed, the thick coils of a huge black snake were slowly heaving forward.

"Good God, what a monster!" With an instinctive gesture of protection against the gliding horror, George gathered the girl into his arms and held her close against him. "I'd have stepped on him and been bitten in another moment. How quick you were, Betsy!" For an instant they listened to the rustling progress as the snake, stunned, but unharmed, glided into the underbrush.

Almost whispering, Betsy said with a shudder, "There are very few of those dangerous snakes left on the island. I never watch out for them. Thank Heaven I saw this one."

Suddenly then they became aware of each other. "Betsy, darling, you're trembling!" said he. Their eyes met and, feeling a blush mounting from her very toes, the girl knew that he longed to kiss her. She recalled the dream aroused by the touch of little Emanuel's lips upon her cheek. She remembered those thrilling words Napoleon had spoken. This tall soldier, holding her so tensely, murmuring an endearment, bending that look upon her, did indeed seem a lover. Shyly she drew back, yet wished the magic moment might last forever.

Carestairs gently relaxed his grasp. As he steadied her she saw that he was pale and incapable of speech and without a word they hurried, hand in hand, past the place where the snake had lain. The silent current of feeling between them swept the girl along as if on wings. In spite of heat and effort, it seemed but a short time until they crossed the ravine, walked up the slope beyond and were in the gardens of Plantation House.

The instant they reached the steps of the shady veranda, Jane came flying out the door. Behind her were Major Fehrzen, looking very anxious, and Mrs. Wilks. Questions, exclamations, reproaches pelted down upon her. She was both too elated and too weary either to listen or reply. Gratefully she followed Mrs. Wilks upstairs where she bathed her face, ordered her hair and had her shoes rubbed and greased by an attentive servant. Now, however, she was conscious of a throbbing pain in her head. In contrast with its hard insistence everything else seemed unreal. She felt herself going down the stairs without touching them and saw the people gathered in the spacious drawing-room as mere shadows.

Afterwards only a few moments of that visit remained distinct. She recalled the beautiful look Mrs. Wilks gave her when told how deeply she would be missed. And she remembered being lifted into a saddle by Colonel Wilks. George was there beside her, too, giving her a grave look, murmuring, "Tomorrow." She had a dim recollection of Major Fehrzen riding close beside her borrowed horse. But how she kept her feet in the stirrups and her knee over the saddle horn, she could not have told. The zigzag stabs of pain came faster and faster. When at last the horses stopped before the Briars' bungalow her will relaxed its grip; she slipped limply from the saddle and beyond that was a long blank.

When at last she woke with a clear head she found she had been ill for several days. The price of her walk across the mountain had been a partial sunstroke.

After the pain was gone, however, convalescence was delightful. To lie against a pile of cushions while the servants, her little brothers, and even Jane gladly ran to do her bidding made her feel a great deal like the Empress Josephine. It was flattering to receive from friends notes and messages and a gorgeous nosegay from Major Fehrzen. But nothing else could match the moment when George Carestairs came riding up.

She was out on the piazza for the first time that afternoon, stretched on a settee with a light afghan over her white frock. When she saw the Ensign dismounting on the lawn she felt a little giddy again. Yet she was able to observe that he was almost too impatient to see about his horse and with a visible effort stopped to pay his respects to Mrs. Balcombe. Then he stood beside Betsy, caught her hand to his lips and looked down at her with eyes brilliant and grave.

"It was just a touch of sun," she murmured. "I'm almost well again."

"Oh, I blame myself! Why didn't you say you were tired and ill," he chided softly. "I should have gone to borrow a horse."

"I did not feel it—truly," she replied, and blushed to remember why.

She heard his sharp intake of breath as he saw that tell-tale flush. She watched him glance around the veranda and turn back with a quick grin because Mrs. Balcombe was crossing the lawn to speak to her husband. Drawing up a chair very close to the settee Carestairs sat down and murmured over and over, "Oh, Betsy, Betsy Balcombe!" It was like an incantation.

Her fingers pulled at a chain around her neck. "I wear your locket all the time," said she and dropped her eyelashes at his look of deep delight.

The sound of a quick step on the veranda was followed by William Balcombe's ringing voice. "Well, my spoiled little madcap, here's a very special gift just arrived. Guess who sent it!"

As the Ensign sprang up to bow, Betsy stretched out eager hands. She took from her father an exquisite small basket of white and gold porcelain with a fitted cover. "Open it, child," said Mr. Balcombe. "I must go and order a glass of wine for the messenger."

Even before he vanished into the house, the girl had lifted the lid and looked into the dish. "Marrons glacés!" she cried in delight. "He remembered my favorite sweet. How wonderful of Boney!"

"Boney! He sent you this? How did he know you were ill—do you communicate with him every day?" Carestairs bent a black look down upon her. "And your father permits you to accept it—indeed, he is pleased!"

She stared up at him in consternation. It had suddenly occurred to her that the quarrel between them might have serious consequences. Suppose George reported unfavorably about her father's friendliness to Napoleon! The uncompromising face of scorn and anger told her he would be quite capable of going that far. Her throat ached with anxiety and with disappointment at the change in her visitor.

"Oh, Betsy, now everything is spoiled!" he raged. "I had in my pocket here"—he tapped his breast—"a little gift for you. But now that you have an 'imperial' trinket—perhaps stolen from Venice or Vienna—it seems unworthy to offer. My wishes and convictions mean nothing to you, do they?" He searched her face as if in hope she might deny it. But as she held her troubled silence, he said abruptly, "I bid you good day, ma'am."

Bowing from the waist, the Ensign strode down the veranda in magnificent form. He had already mounted his horse and was galloping off when William Balcombe came out of the hall. The latter's startled eyes fled from that retreating figure to Betsy. In an instant he was beside her.

"Don't look like that, little girl. He is not worth it. What happened? Did you quarrel?"

Faintly she replied, "He cannot bear to have me friends with Boney. He thinks it is treachery." She held up the basket of marrons as mute evidence. "Oh, father, if the new Governor feels the same way, it will be dangerous to have anything to do with Napoleon."

William Balcombe sat down beside her. For an instant, with shadowed face, he stared down at the floor. "It hardly seems likely," he said at last. "Both Admiral Cockburn and Sir George Bingham have been glad enough to dine at Longwood and be friendly. And yet—one never knows. There is gunpowder in the situation and things have started badly. If young Carestairs was so upset by a box of confections, he has doubtless heard—since everything leaks out—the several ways in which General Bonaparte has just affronted the British representatives."

Betsy listened eagerly to her father's account. For in spite of the misery in her heart, some margin of herself remained free to appreciate the great human drama she touched so closely.

First was the fiasco of Sir Hudson Lowe's initial visit to Longwood. He went up there, of course, with Admiral Cockburn who expected to introduce him to Napoleon. But somehow after Marchand, the chief valet, had announced both dignitaries and the lackey had opened the drawing-room door, Sir Hudson alone was admitted and the door closed in the furious Admiral's face. In answer to his protests the lackey said that so far as he knew only the Governor had been announced. Afterwards Count Bertrand declared it was a misunderstanding between the servants.

But everyone believed Napoleon had ordered this to happen just to annoy the Admiral and to stir up trouble. Sir Hudson Lowe had been too intent on the interview to realize that to go in by himself was a breach of etiquette. But he was aghast to learn later of the rudeness offered his colleague.

The second episode was considered far worse. Napoleon had addressed to the Prince Regent of England a letter, supposed by all to be full of grievances. He asked that it not be submitted to the censorship at Plantation House, where all his mail was read before forwarding, but instead that it be sent sealed. Permission was refused. Thereupon he sent one of his staff to ask Colonel Wilks to carry the sealed letter in person to England when he sailed. The Colonel considered the request an insult. For it implied that he would secretly do something in direct opposition to the rulings of both his successor and of Admiral Cockburn. Naturally the messenger was haughtily repulsed.

"Even yesterday," Mr. Balcombe concluded, "there was fresh cause for irritation. When Sir Hudson Lowe rode over to Longwood, General Bonaparte flatly refused to see him and merely sent word that he was indisposed. So you see, Betsy, he has thrown down a gauntlet of defiance. He considers every regulation a grievance. For he continues to assert that he is not legitimately a prisoner and should not be treated as one."

"What do you think is going to happen?" asked Betsy fearfully.

After a thoughtful silence, her father replied, "It all depends on the humanity of the ruling powers. I believe that along with unabated precaution against Boney's escape, there might go a certain bigness of heart. But one must remember that throughout all Europe this man has inspired terror and hatred. After all, he has not exactly set us an example of how to love one's enemies."

For many days Betsy pondered that phrase, bigness of heart. It was exactly what she missed in George Carestairs. Often she thought of him with something akin to hate. But against this lack she weighed his courage, his patriotism and the manly worth which Napoleon had praised when they had observed him at work. Really, however, something far more electric than such qualities kept his image constantly before her. Resentfully she tried to banish it and was thankful for all the excitement of her birthday ball.

That night of May 9, 1816, was memorable for many reasons. For one thing, it was exceptionally beautiful. Luminous twilight was succeeded by a moon which sailed high over the filmy scarf of cloud flung off by the warm earth. Moreover, such gaiety possessed all the guests that antagonisms were buried. Madame Bertrand danced with all the officers and Gourgaud with all the young ladies.

Betsy, wearing her new frock of China silk embroidered in flowers, made good use of her legitimate claim to the center of the stage. She was thrilled with joy that at her party for the first time on St. Helena a new form of dancing was introduced. The girl found it easy to learn and intoxicating to execute. They called it the waltz. She had not anticipated such a good time—not after George Carestairs' cold little note which said that he would be on duty in the boat patrol around the island. For what was the value of a glamorous scene if not to affect him? Her enjoyment of the evening's comedy was entirely due to its overture.

General Gourgaud, who came early, looking resplendent in his gold epaulettes and sword, took Betsy aside. In her ear he murmured that General Bonaparte and his escort, who had accompanied Gourgaud to the Briars, still lingered near the boundaries. "I think, mademoiselle,"

said the Frenchman, "the Emperor would be glad to salute you on your natal day."

The next moment Betsy was flying down the driveway.
Beyond the gate in the twilight she saw the figures of the
two horsemen. They were just beginning to descend the
steep side road. But at her shout they halted and turned
their horses back. Waiting for them an instant Betsy recalled that she had rushed out to meet the person who
had just insulted all her father's official superiors. Yet the
moment the familiar green coat leaned from the saddle
she felt the gush of all her old excitement and warmth.

"Ah, Mees Betsee, all my felicitations."

He drew off his glove and she seized his hand in both
hers. At the same instant, with an oblique glance at the
escort, she recognized Captain Poppleton.

The Englishman smiled and bowed. "Good evening,
Miss Balcombe. I am glad you are well again," he said
pleasantly.

"Oui, oui! I understand what Poppleton says and I also
am glad," said Napoleon. "Your little note about the marrons was very well composed. You have profited by our
lessons. I am pleased that you liked Piron's confections.
You must come and eat more soon."

Swept by delight in his presence the girl cried impulsively, "Why don't you come to my party? Ride in,
both of you, if only for a moment! The pavilion looks
magnificent with all its flags and lanterns, monsieur
le Général. You ought to see the guests assembling in
your former bedroom."

Napoleon chuckled. "You have grown older by the
calendar, ma petite, but you still talk like a child—n'est-

[183]

ce pas, Capitaine? Turn around! Let me regard the new frock. Ah, oui, c'est charmante. Have you seen the wife of Sir Hudson? Gourgaud came back from meeting Lady Lowe at Madame Bertrand's, quite eloquent about her costume."

Betsy was charmed by his gossip. "Yes, monsieur le Général, mother took me to call at Plantation House recently. Lady Lowe is very gracious, very handsome. I have not yet met her husband."

"Do you know what Dr. Warden said to me?" Again Napoleon chuckled. "I asked him if he had observed the face of the new Governor and whether he found it pleasing. The doctor replied, 'If I am to speak the truth, I like Lady Lowe's far better.' Voilà—a man of taste. I am sure you will agree, Betsee. Nobody could like that hangman." The speaker reached down and pulled the girl's ear. "When are you coming to see me again? I moost spik for you the English. How do you doo? Gudebyee! Doo you lak me? Mon dieu, it is difficult!"

What a mischievous devil looked down at her out of his eyes! Nobody was so much fun. Betsy caught his hand again, hating to let him go. Even at his worst, he seemed much more alive than anyone else. "If you won't come in," she cried, "you must wait here until I bring you a piece of birthday cake—you and Captain Poppleton." At his movement of dissent she cried furiously, "You *must* have some. Otherwise I shall be heartbroken."

As she ran back up the driveway and into the house, newly arrived guests tried to greet her. But, without stopping, she only laughed over her shoulder and bade them wait a moment. On the return trip she was conscious of curious glances and whispers. But she cared not a whit. Her spirits were soaring once more. The most famous man in the world had munched a piece of her cake, patted her head and told her he missed her sorely. Could any girl have had a more marvelous birthday present?

Now she could take the entire party to her heart and love it. Without stopping for breath she danced every instant. Even when the clock struck one she was quite sorry to see the servants arrive to set up the supper tables. But she found it terribly thrilling to have all the men rise and drink her health with a clink of glasses and a clatter of swords. For more than an hour while corks popped and viands were passed, the elaborate meal went on. Betsy, seated beside the Governor's aide, Major Gorrequer, was told about many projects which his chief had worked out for Napoleon's comfort. Pipes were to bring down from Diana's Peak plenty of water for his luxurious hot baths. Plans for a new house were being discussed. A boat-load of furniture had been ordered.

Listening in surprise, the girl recalled Napoleon's violent phrase about the Governor. Surely such consideration was not the spirit of a "hangman." She wondered what thoughts about the situation Major Gorrequer hid behind his smooth, sphinx-like face and crooked smile. When, in order to test him, she spoke of Dr. O'Meara, the Major's expression never changed. Yet he certainly must have known that already the fiery Irishman was at odds with Sir Hudson Lowe. The doctor had confided to Betsy in the heat of indignation that the Governor wanted him to report in detail all his private conversations at Longwood.

"Lowe would have me act the part, not of a physician, but a spy," O'Meara had growled furiously.

Immediately after supper was over many of the guests departed. Others remained dancing until the first streaks of dawn appeared in the east. Long before that Mrs. Balcombe, tired to death, had slipped away. She left her husband to serve as chaperon. But that cordial host, pouring out drinks and swapping stories with the older men, had lost his sharp sense of what was going on. He merely looked amused when Major Fehrzen and Betsy came up to him with their extraordinary request. Might Betsy be permitted to ride to Jamestown with those who were homeward bound, get a sniff of the sea and ride back with the Major?

"It will do your daughter good, you know, Mr. Balcombe," pled the officer. "After she returns she will sleep like a kitten. I promise to take perfect care of her."

"Yes, do that," commanded Mr. Balcombe earnestly and turned back to his companions.

Betsy was thoroughly shocked. Occasionally she had heard her mother make unguarded complaints and Napoleon speak teasingly on the subject, but never in her life before had she seen her father affected by drink. She hesitated to take advantage of his careless dismissal. But the Major, making light of her scruples, assured her that the most sober father would agree to so innocent a plan. Thus heartened by a man she completely trusted, Betsy fled swiftly down to the house to change her clothes.

It was a greater temptation than she could resist to show off her new riding outfit—the first she had ever possessed. The long, voluminous skirt and buttoned jacket were of matching green cloth and the little boots and high beaver hat were black. Before she blew out the candle and stole down the stairs, she noted in the mirror that she had never looked so grown up. It was hardly surprising to find she could pass Jane on the veranda without being recognized in the half light of dawn.

Greeted with cheers by the mounted group on the lawn, she strutted before them. "Father had these clothes made for my birthday," she crowed. "Are they not lovely?"

With much merriment the party rode off. But hardly had they reached the main road when Betsy's gaiety vanished. It was as if the cold mist and wind sweeping up the valley had blown it all away. What did any of these pranks matter, she asked herself, without George Carestairs to share them? The memory of how his arms had gone around her on the mountainside stabbed her with longing to recapture that magic. To the lively remarks of Fehrzen who rode beside her she tossed absent-minded monosyllables.

Glancing at her face after a silence the Major said suddenly, almost as if he had read her thoughts, "Lucky for me Carestairs had to miss your lovely ball, Betsy. Otherwise, he'd be carrying you off as he did last time— getting you moon-struck tonight. Yet I pity him out there rowing about on the cold sea all night, poor devil! I'll admit he is an excellent soldier beneath that lordly manner that women like so much."

Ah, yes, she silently agreed. He was the sort of person men respected. As for his masterfulness, she knew she liked quite as much as hated it.

Through the village street the horses went clattering. A few lanterns still flickered wanly at the doors. Out of one upper window a night-capped head was thrust out to gape at the cavalcade. When they reached the Marino, where everyone scattered with a final outburst of farewells, Betsy dismounted to get close to the sea. While her companion fastened the horses, she strolled in the direction of the landing steps. Observing a group of figures down there, she wondered whether they were fishermen who had managed to slip past the guards and get out to their nets.

Then with quickening pulse she realized that something more was going on than the mere beaching of a heavy boat. The men were halloing and making signals to the sentries about the Castle. In response three soldiers came running along the moat wall and at the same time, with a creak and groan, the drawbridge began to descend.

As the distant group started forward Betsy had a weird sense that whatever had happened concerned her. Yet nothing definite explained the feeling until she saw that these were not fishermen, but sailors who bent beneath a burden. In another instant she knew what they carried. It was a man's body stretched out on a board. Simultaneously with this recognition echoed deep in her heart a cry of terror, "George! He has been drowned!"

With that her mind seemed to split in two. One part, narrowing to a single fear, was intensely alive. The other received impressions in a dream. In vain Major Fehrzen tried to get her away. Now she heard the tramp of feet upon the bridge. Next she realized that the destination of the bearers was the Castle Terrace. Before her companion could stop her, she flew up the stone steps and reached the portico by the time the men had laid down their load. Her living self without surprise went out to meet the still, white face of George Carestairs. But that other consciousness could mark the beauty of the carven features and the lines of the inert form molded in soaking garments. With hands folded on his breast he was a young knight dead in the course of duty!

She was being stared at. The sailors were muttering. Fehrzen came leaping across the terrace. Something fierce in her defied them all. But it was not yet grief. With one swift movement she knelt beside the prostrate figure and put her hand on his. Instantly her mind grew whole again. Those hands were warm! At her touch the closed eyes opened for a flash, the pale lips parted, half smiled and moved to form her name.

"It's only shock, miss," vouchsafed one of the sailors. "Did you think he be drownded? He'll come around soon."

Betsy sank to the flagstones, still holding those warm hands and tears ran down her cheeks. But she clearly heard what another sailor was saying in answer to a question from the Major.

"Well, sir, plenty happened out there while we were rowing on patrol. We had a time—shot at and half drowned. Wind and waves to break your heart. When the lookout on the point challenged us for the countersign we couldn't make him hear in the gale. So he fired twice—once wide, as a warning. Still we couldn't pull up nearer without being swamped. So the guard, according to orders, fired again and nigh wrecked the boat. The

Ensign here was hit by a flying splinter and knocked overboard. But we hauled him back and he brought us safe round the point again. Just now getting through the surf, a roller knocked him against the gunwale and finished him off for a bit. But he'll be fit as a fiddle after a hot drink and a sleep."

At this moment a sentry flung open the Castle door. On the threshold stood an officer sleepily rubbing his eyes. Then he stared. "God save us—what's this? Young Carestairs?" As a half dozen voices assured him the Ensign was very much alive, he gave the sharp command, "Bring him in!"

Up went the board in a twinkling. Feet shuffled. The great door banged. In an instant Betsy and the Major had been left alone in the portico.

She stood up. Confusion and fatigue made a humming in her ears. If she were only on her horse this moment, riding home alone! But there was Major Fehrzen standing close, looking at her strangely. She thought he might be laughing at her for being such a little fool. But he spoke quietly out of his heart, as if they two were quite alone on the globe.

"You are in love with Carestairs, aren't you, Betsy? Does he know it?"

She could not reply. His words went through her with a silver shock which made her quiver from head to foot. "Please take me home!" she gasped.

Immediately she felt the comfort of an arm sustaining her. And in the next half hour, without another word to intrude upon the whirl of her thoughts, she experienced a friendliness which from that time forward set Major

Fehrzen quite apart from everyone else. He even had the kindness to drop in for tea in the late afternoon when Betsy was downstairs again after a long sleep. Casually to the assembled family he announced what was important to her alone. Ensign Carestairs, after an episode which had proved him a gallant officer, was resting quietly in the marine hospital. He was not badly injured and would soon be on duty again.

Yet it was weeks before the vision of a young man cold in death could be replaced by a sight of him in full health. Betsy had to keep up her rôle of a girl untroubled by emotion deeper than the day. Luckily events followed one upon another to ease the task. First, the Skeltons left in a great whirl of farewell parties. Then Jamestown seethed with the excitement of having a fleet from India anchor for two days to take on supplies. Every passenger who landed determined to see Napoleon and the officials were bombarded with requests to visit Longwood. These were refused. But on hired nags a stream of people rode up past the gate all day long in the vain hope of catching a mere glimpse of the celebrated figure. The fleet's most august passenger, however, was immediately received at Plantation House and a ceremonial dinner was planned in her honor. She was the Countess of Loudon, wife of the Governor in Chief of Bengal.

That dinner caused a fresh uproar concerning Napoleon. And Betsy heard the very beginning of it at Madame Bertrand's. She and her mother had gone up to Huts Gate for tea the day the English Countess landed. While they were there an officer close to Sir Hudson Lowe stopped in to pay his respects to the Grand Marshal and his wife. But Count Bertrand, as usual, was at Longwood.

During the course of conversation about the fleet, the officer said, "Our new Governor is uncommonly magnanimous. He is determined that General Bonaparte shall not remain in a state of personal enmity with him. Consequently Sir Hudson has sent over to Longwood the very first invitation to his dinner for Countess Loudon tomorrow night. The messenger has just preceded me down the road."

"An invitation to Plantation House?" gasped Madame Bertrand. "For the Emperor?"

Betsy was not sure how to interpret her amazement. But the Colonel had no such vagueness. "Yes, madam," said he complaisantly, "the Governor has done him that honor."

His hostess flushed. *"Him* the honor!" she repeated with soft sarcasm. "Remember, Colonel, this invitation is the first social recognition advanced from Sir Hudson Lowe. Believe me, I think what is in his mind is pleasing his visitor rather than the Emperor."

"Well, be that as it may," returned the officer imperturbably, "I am sure the occasion will be an interesting one for all who are privileged to be present. There must be a million people alive who would give a large sum to dine with the man who made and unmade kings."

Betsy heard him with a swift leap of gratitude for all her own coveted privileges. Then her thoughts raced on to the consequences of this affair. The instant the Colonel had taken his leave Madame Bertrand turned to Mrs. Balcombe and said, "The Emperor will never accept, mark my words."

The prophecy was vindicated in a short time. For Count Bertrand came in obviously excited. Assuring him that the visitors were already aware of the situation, his wife bade him tell what had occurred at Longwood. In a rapid whisper Betsy translated his remarks to her mother.

"When Marchand delivered the Governor's card to me," said the Grand Marshal, "I immediately took it in to the Emperor. He opened it, read it without change of expression and handed it to me. But after I had read and returned it, he gave it back again. 'Sire,' I asked, 'what answer is it your Majesty's pleasure to send?' Already he was once more absorbed in the manuscript of his dictated memoirs which he had been reading. There was a moment's silence. Then he replied in an indifferent voice, 'Say the Emperor gave no answer.'"

"But the Governor will be furious," cried Madame Bertrand, throwing out her lovely hands.

Her husband shrugged. "He has only himself to blame for his presumption. Does he expect to command his Majesty's presence at will? Imagine the Emperor going to a dinner party under guard! Sir Hudson Lowe has no delicacy of mind."

Betsy recalled with a sharp twinge of conscience that only the week before she had begged Napoleon to come to her ball. With what humor he had turned off her childish impulse! Indeed, he always managed to impress her as being so gay and free that she realized only with a start that he was neither. To do so weighed her down with sadness.

As she made her adieux that afternoon in her mother's wake, Count Bertrand said to her with his stiff little bow,

"Today at breakfast, mademoiselle, the Emperor asked me to invite you and your sister to luncheon next week on Wednesday. I shall send a pass. His Majesty has received a beautiful present which he would like to show you."

That occasion was destined to produce a variety of emotions—joy and sadness, hilarity and a certain excitement. Moreover, before she left Longwood that day, Betsy was fated to have an encounter which proved prophetic of disaster.

STORMS OVER LONGWOOD

"The Emperor is in the billiard room working on his maps, mesdemoiselles," announced Marchand. "He left word that you both were to be admitted when you came."

As the valet turned to lead the way Jane made a little face of disgust. From the beginning she had opposed accepting this luncheon engagement at Longwood. "It won't be amusing enough for the risk of incurring the Governor's disapproval," she had said. Now she whispered to Betsy, "Oh, those tiresome military maps! I'd rather look at his books."

The trio were almost at the billiard-room door, when it flew open and General Gourgaud, with a face black as thunder, rushed out. Seeing who were behind the valet, he stopped short. But some fury in him was too great for the possibility of a smile. The most he could do was to bow stiffly and stride furiously on. Before the girls had time even to wonder what had angered him, they heard Marchand announce in what Betsy called his "palace" voice, "Votre Majesté, les mesdemoiselles Balcombe." Immediately they were ushered into the room.

It looked at this moment more like a workshop than a place for games. The billiard-table was strewn with notes and manuscript. Standing on a stool in order to reach the highest of all the many maps stretched along the wall, Las Cases was in the act of sticking red and green pins into certain spots according to the dictates of his chief.

Just as the visitors crossed the threshold Napoleon was saying in a ringing tone, "Non, non! More to the left. Farther from the mountains. The battle took place on level ground."

Obediently Las Cases moved the pins and the Commander of the French Armies turned around. "Eh, bien, mes enfants, bonjour! Voilà! You arrive on the eve of battle. The guns roar and the bugle is sounding the charge. Descend, Las Cases, that the young ladies may see!"

After making her curtsies Betsy took a step forward and stared curiously at the elaborately drawn maps. She had often thought of the morning in the summerhouse when she had seen Napoleon as the formidable warrior, careless of the human cost of victory. Now, almost shuddering, she said, "Tell me, monsieur le Général, does each pin represent a soldier?"

He laughed. "Non, ma petite, a thousand soldiers. The red ones are mine and the green belong to Austria. I am trying to learn whether I could have bettered my plan of action."

In astonishment she asked, "Can you really remember every move you made, monsieur?"

Impatient fingers snapped in air. "That is easy. What is

difficult is to judge the situation afresh. If only I could discuss the matter with someone equally versed in tactics."

"But, your Majesty," protested Las Cases, smiling, "that would be impossible under any circumstances. You have no equal on earth." He shot a glance at Betsy, defying her to think of Wellington. But some time ago she had been half-convinced by Gourgaud that the Allies' victory at Waterloo was due to superior numbers and to the mistakes of certain French Generals.

Napoleon's reply was a shrug and he continued to study the map in silence. With her eyes on his absorbed face the girl had a sharp sense of the isolation of greatness. This man's genius had always set him apart. Here it left him with no one capable of sharing his thoughts.

Suddenly from the other end of the room floated Jane's voice. "It's raining. Isn't that odd when the sun was so hot at the Briars?"

Napoleon wrenched his eyes from the battle line. "Mees Jeanne does not like my beautiful maps," he cried accusingly. "She prefers to stare out the window at that sad mountain." Then as Jane, with a look of embarrassment, moved toward him, he smiled forgivingly. "Yes, mademoiselle, it rains here if nowhere else on the island and that does little to lift the spirits. But we must try to be lively. Perhaps a game of billiards or—"

He broke off at the entrance of Count Bertrand. Betsy observed that the Grand Marshal had a constrained and hesitating air and that his chief stiffened at the sight of him. In silence Bertrand presented a card. Napoleon looked at the name and sniffed. "Say that the Emperor is engaged."

[197]

When, without uttering a word, the Count bowed and retreated, Betsy wondered afresh what on earth had so upset the household. Before luncheon she found out. For after the billiard game she was permitted on request to dash out to the stables for a glimpse of the horses, and there, giving directions to Archambaud, the groom, she found General Gourgaud.

His smile was a sarcastic glare. "Behold in me the Master of the Horse!" he cried mockingly.

Betsy sought for something soothing to say. "But is not that position one of great honor?"

"Oh, yes, in time of war. My predecessor was no less a person than Caulaincourt, the Duke of Vicenza. But here? Bah! It is nothing. Everyone else gets more than I. This morning the Emperor even assigned the false Las Cases a task belonging by rights to me. I had taken the dictation on that campaign and I should have been the one to place the pins on the map."

As if Betsy's expression made him ashamed of the petty complaint, he dropped his head and muttered, "There are too many of us here—too many servants, too large a staff —for the few duties which can be contrived."

Curiosity prompted the girl to take advantage of this confidential mood. "And why is Count Bertrand in disfavor?" she asked.

"Hah, you noticed it! He has long been contending with his Majesty over the conduct of Madame Bertrand. She has frequently dined with Admiral Cockburn and now that he is leaving so soon, this occurs still more often. Last night she was expected here for dinner and the servants actually waited for her. When the Emperor discovered why the meal was late, he was in a fine rage. Bertrand says that if anything in this terrible place can divert the young and charming woman who is his wife, he is not going to deprive her of it. The Emperor was deeply wounded. He declared that such a thing would not have happened in the old days of glory, but that now in his fallen state, he is disregarded."

Aware that the luncheon hour was at hand, the two had begun to stroll back to the house. Betsy said nothing, but she was thinking hard about Count Bertrand. Never would she have guessed that the mild little man would defend a woman's liberty of action with such vigor.

With irritable fingers Gourgaud jerked a leaf from a cabbage tree. "We are in confusion here also," he continued, "because of the papers Sir Hudson Lowe has commanded us to sign. We are obliged either to pledge ourselves to stay during the Emperor's lifetime or make up our minds to go to Cape Town."

"Go?" echoed Betsy in a shocked tone. "Tiens! You would not leave him now, would you?"

"I cannot think I am needed," replied the young man mournfully. "There are plenty of people to flatter and agree. I am too honest to be a courtier." He added in a choked voice, "And I should like to see my mother."

During the luncheon he hardly looked up from his plate. And, indeed, the meal began in so dull a fashion that Betsy quite envied Emanuel Las Cases. His father remarked that the boy had gone off with little Tristram Montholon and Napoleon Bertrand for a picnic party in the woods. Presently Count Montholon began to talk about the departure of the Admiral and all the new officials due to arrive any day. Sir Pultney Malcom, who was to take Sir George Cockburn's place, was coming with Lady Malcom on the *Newcastle*. On the same vessel were the Commissioners from Europe.

None of this was news to the daughters of William Balcombe. The Chief Purveyor on St. Helena was naturally always involved in arranging accommodations for new officials. At the Briars they had talked for weeks about the International Commission appointed to share England's responsibility for the safeguarding of Napoleon. Russia, Austria and France were each to send a representative. The Austrian Baron was bringing his wife and the island colony's expectations from such cosmopolitan society were soaring high.

For his part, Napoleon had every air of having heard all this gossip before. Not until Las Cases mentioned the current situation in Europe did his chief's face brighten. Then all at once he came to life.

"The journals Dr. O'Meara brought spoke of the restlessness in France," he said gloatingly. "King Louis is well-hated. The French, like women, must be cajoled with flattery, not merely ordered about. Voyons, I shall be needed yet to take the helm. Yes, my dear Gourgaud, have patience. We may be sent for in such a way that England dare not refuse to send us back. Then there will be plenty for you to do with your energy and loyalty." He tossed him a smile and Betsy saw the poor fellow seize upon it as a hungry dog snatches up a bone.

With that Napoleon rose with his usual abruptness and took his visitors into the drawing-room. There he showed them the gift received from England which Count Bertrand had mentioned to Betsy. It was a set of chessmen in ivory, exquisitely carved. The knights, encased in armor, rode horses elaborately caparisoned and each pawn wore the costume of a different nationality.

Betsy hung over them fascinated. "Who sent you these, monsieur?" she asked.

"Lord Keith's brother, Mr. Elphinstone. His daughter is Lady Malcom who is coming here. I saved his son's life on the battlefield about a year ago. The young officer lay wounded on the ground in the path of the cavalry and I had him carried to the rear and attended by my physician. It was nothing. Often have I done more for a wounded enemy. But the Elphinstones are kindly disposed in consequence."

Betsy stole a glance at the face, beautiful in its gravity, which bent over the table. A year ago was the battle of Waterloo—a year almost to the day. Then an empire was lost and a fate was sealed by a struggle so fierce and bloody that even to think of it made the head reel. Now the cause of that tremendous uproar sat here at the world's end, fingering ivory toys. And his vast combat was reduced to a quarrel between two of his household over red and green pins. With such thoughts going through her head Betsy was in no mood for cheerful pranks and was grateful to have her sister lift the weight of the moment.

"Are we not to be shown the rest of your apartments, monsieur?" asked Jane with a hint of impatience. "And visit Madame Montholon? I should love to see her new baby."

"Mais oui, certainement!" With alacrity, as if he also

[201]

were glad to be diverted, Napoleon sprang to his feet.

By the time they entered Madame Montholon's room, he seemed in lively spirits once more. While the Countess from her couch watched in helpless fright, he took the tiny infant from the nurse and swung it up and down.

"Look out! You will drop her, monsieur!" cried Betsy, alarmed at his casual handling.

"Nonsense!" he jeered, tossing the baby higher. "I have often played this way with the little King of Rome. Only at this age do I like little girls," he shot a mischievous look at his critic. "When they reach fourteen years, they become impertinent monkeys who cause one much trouble." Placing the baby in her mother's lap, he laughed and pulled Betsy's ears.

In revenge she jerked off a loose gold bugle from the sleeve of his coat and with a triumphant cry, darted out of the room. As she dashed down the corridor she heard him coming behind her.

But, unlike former days, flight and pursuit were only half-hearted. When the pair rushed into the drawing-room to find Dr. O'Meara waiting there, Betsy stopped short to curtsey and Napoleon, panting a little, flung himself into an armchair. He greeted the doctor in Italian and for some time rapid talk passed back and forth between the two. The girl, who understood no word of it, was amusing herself with the wonderful chessmen when she heard the murmured sound of her name. Quickly glancing up she met from each pair of eyes the same concentrated look.

She crossed the room. "What is it, monsieur le Général? What did monsieur le docteur say about me?"

Napoleon held out his hand with one of his rare smiles of pure sweetness, and she stood beside his chair like a little girl. "A few days ago," said he, "I was told a story that interested me very much. It concerned a young English officer who, although hurt during his patrol on the water, proved himself stout-hearted and resourceful. Just now I asked for news of him and the doctor, in giving it, said the Ensign is interested in you. I knew at once he is the one we passed that afternoon at Deadwood, is it not so?"

In dismay Betsy felt herself beginning to tremble. She withdrew from the soft grasp upon her hand and, turning swiftly to O'Meara, asked in English, "Is there news of him, doctor? What is it?"

Gently the Irish voice replied, "Only today, Betsy, it was decided to send young Carestairs to Cape Town on a small mission. Really it is for his health. He recovers slowly and the hospital surgeon thought the sea trip and change of air would do him good. A boat happens to have anchored today en route to the Cape and they are putting him on it."

Maidenly reserve had never been instinctive with Betsy. Now it deserted her entirely. With a bound she confronted the doctor. Seizing the velvet lapels of his purple coat, she gave them a little shake. "You mean—" she gasped, "he leaves today?"

"Probably at dawn tomorrow."

"Ah!" Her nervous hands flew over her heart. For an instant one wild impulse after another took possession of her. She would ride straight down to the hospital. She would go to the village tomorrow at sunrise and see him off. She would send old Toby with a message. She couldn't let him go like this without a word—not with that last picture of him haunting her day and night. Yet all the while some deeper sanity warned her sternly that she had no choice but to accept in silence.

"He will return ere long, Betsy," remarked O'Meara with matter-of-fact comfort. "And in his absence other young officers will have some opportunity to interest you. A captivating young lady, is this one, General Bonaparte."

Betsy, conscious that Napoleon was watching her curiously, saw with relief both doors into the drawing-room open simultaneously. Jane, who must have been talking all this time with Madame Montholon, came through one, a valet in gold and green livery through the other. The servant announced that Dr. Warden was with General Gourgaud and that he wished to leave his adieux.

"Ah, oui! The doctor is sailing back to England," exclaimed Napoleon. "I must say good-by to him. Ask him to go into the library, Santini. Mesdemoiselles, my good friend O'Meara will see you to your horses."

Briefly Jane thanked him, wished him good health and left the room. Betsy, still dazed with shock, followed her blindly without so much as a curtsey for her host. Unconscious of what she was doing, she walked straight out through the entrance room and started not in the direction of the stables but toward the Guard House. A familiar shout stopped her.

"Mees Betsee! You have forgotten to say farewell."

Napoleon, with O'Meara beside him, was standing outside the door. Back she ran, filled with compunction, to take his hand and murmur her apologies. She felt her cheek playfully slapped and heard O'Meara's deep chuckle. Then abruptly those friendly faces changed. With a low ejaculation Napoleon vanished through the doorway and the doctor, seizing Betsy's arm, drew her off toward the rear of the house. She managed, however, to turn a curious head. Near the gate in red coat, trimmed with gold lace, in white breeches, high boots and plumed hat, stood a tall man. The girl saw the wide, thin mouth under a long nose turn downward and felt a piercing glance fixed upon her. She did not need her companion's exclamation to tell her that this must be Sir Hudson Lowe.

"What is he here for—without warning or appointment?" growled the Irishman as he strode along. Meeting Count Bertrand on the green behind the house, he repeated the question.

The Grand Marshal shrugged. "The Governor has not asked to see the Emperor. He may have come up to inquire how the work on the water pipe line progresses."

As the two girls rode out of the gate a few moments later, Betsy looked sharply about. There he was again at the window of the sentry's lodge. Once more she had the impression of estimating eyes looking out from an obdurate face. They had told her that her part in the intimate scene with Napoleon and his stubborn doctor had been duly noted. That glance placed her on the side of the Governor's enemies. He doubtless already knew from the sentry that she was William Balcombe's daughter.

Not a word of this encounter did she utter to her sister. Jane, all unaware of it, was repeating the gossip concerning the quarrelsome Longwood household gleaned from

Madame Montholon. Betsy did not listen. For the first mile she was busy hating Sir Hudson Lowe and his jailer's air. Then her thoughts, flying back to George Carestairs, released her pent-up despair.

How could she bear his leaving? Life on St. Helena would have no more glamour. Besides—she suddenly recalled Napoleon's peculiar expression when he saw how distracted she had been. Boney didn't believe the Ensign was really her lover—that was plain. He looked as if he were sorry for a girl jilted in love. Was he right? Oh, what if he were right?

Later that evening, however, she was upbraiding herself for lack of faith. Major Fehrzen brought her a letter which, for all its Eighteenth Century stiffness, dispelled her doubts. George made it clear that every instant awake and asleep he had thought of her face, as he had seen it bent tenderly over him there on the terrace. He warned her that should he come back to find that she had forgotten him and was cherishing another in his place, he would care to live no longer. In short, it was altogether a most satisfactory communication.

Even so, had Betsy realized when she read it how many months George was to be away, she would have felt heartsick. But, reassured by his letter, she allowed herself to be distracted by the events following his departure. Dr. Warden's leaving was soon eclipsed by the farewells offered Admiral Cockburn and the welcome given his successor, Sir Pultney Malcom. As for the foreign Commissioners, they were the subject of endless discussion. When she first met them, Betsy considered the Frenchman an old fop of the first order and the other two rather pompous and dull. Their presence on St. Helena seemed chiefly destined to expand the prevailing spirit of intrigue. Napoleon absolutely refused to receive them except as private individuals. For he would not acknowledge the right of their governments to appoint them for such a purpose. All they could report about his situation was what they were told by Sir Hudson Lowe.

Nevertheless, toward the end of summer Betsy made a surprising discovery about the wife of the Austrian Commissioner, Baroness Sturmer. It served to redeem a rather dreadful afternoon at Plantation House. Inasmuch as Mrs. Balcombe and Jane were themselves receiving guests at the Briars, the girl had ridden over to tea by herself and afterwards felt that advantage was taken of this fact. She had not been there long when Sir Hudson Lowe, to whom she had been presented once or twice previously, managed to get her off in a corner of the drawing-room. Under cover of passing her the cakes, he had thereupon pelted her with questions.

How recently had she been at Longwood? When she mentioned the date the Governor nodded. Apparently he was checking her word against the record of visitors sent him by Count Bertrand. Next the Governor asked if she had not found General Bonaparte in good health and taking walks in the garden, and whether reports of his feeling ill were not much exaggerated.

Betsy tried to fix his pale eyes, but found them restlessly shifting from her to his stepdaughter, Charlotte Johnson, who was talking with Count Balmain, the Commissioner from Russia. Betsy found herself cordially disliking the man's voice and the red hairs on the backs of his hands. "I think the reports are true, sir," she replied. "We were only able to see the General a few moments. He did not look at all like himself and Baron Gourgaud said he had spent four hours in his bath to ease his discomfort."

At this Sir Hudson had compressed his lips glumly and, as soon as courtesy permitted, he left her for his other guests. She watched him go with divided feelings. For well she knew his was no easy lot. Only the week before he had been treated to a terrific scene at Longwood where, fulfilling orders from London, he had gone to lodge a protest against the vast expenditures of the establishment. Napoleon's reply was to call the Governor a hired assassin. Pacing up and down in anger he accused the British Government of wishing to starve the man it illegally held prisoner. On the other hand, said he, the regiment would take his part. All he need do was to go to the camp at Deadwood and say, "The oldest soldier in Europe begs to join your mess." Sir Hudson in desperation answered that he was going to apply for recall and Napoleon heartily commended the idea. The next time the Governor rode over for an interview, he was told that Napoleon was too ill to be seen.

Betsy had heard, also, through Gourgaud that the required papers had not yet been signed by the Longwood staff. Officers and servants alike hesitated to declare their intention of remaining indefinitely on St. Helena. Mr. Balcombe had often said that no Governor would be liked by the French and with this his daughter agreed. But now, as she watched Sir Hudson Lowe moving among his guests with a mechanical smile on his thin lips, she thought his air of suspicion combined with a sense of importance was particularly irritating.

Certainly his wife was far more suave. Yet as the girl went to bid her good-by, she encountered another broadside of questions. Looking over her fan with a vivacious smile, Lady Lowe said, "People tell me, Miss Betsy, that you are quite a favorite with General Bonaparte. Do you really consider him charming? What do you like about him? Tell me what you do when you go to see him?"

Somehow, in spite of the smile, those questions seemed more hostile than friendly. Betsy was stung into using her wits. Smiling in her turn, she replied, "Why do you not consult Lady Malcom, ma'm? She says that after all the dreadful things she had heard of Napoleon she was pleased to find his expression so good and kind and his manner so full of charm. You would find great interest in his conversation, ma'm—of that I am sure."

Before her hostess rallied for a new attack, Betsy had curtsied and made her adieux. Tremulous from this effort the girl went out on the arm of Major Fehrzen to mount her pony, and found the Austrian Commissioner and his wife waiting to ride home with her for a call upon Mrs. Balcombe. They talked little on the way, but Betsy felt the Baroness sliding glances at her every few moments. "She too is suspicious of me," thought the girl and once more felt a fear that her father would suffer through his daughter's friendship for Boney.

On their arrival at the Briars, however, Baroness Sturmer seemed only gracious and sweet. Betsy, who had always admired her looks, watched her and wondered. Presently, to her surprise, the visitor asked to be shown the place where General Bonaparte had stayed and Betsy was assigned the honor. All the way up to the pavilion she was answering eager questions about Napoleon's days at the Briars. As they entered the door her companion seized Betsy's hand convulsively and looked about with eyes grown large with emotion.

Almost in a whisper she said, "So this is where he lived!" After a moment she turned to the girl and said in a low, rapid tone, "You are his friend, I know. You admire him. I wish to tell you—to explain—I was born a French woman and—in my heart—I have never ceased to be the Emperor's loyal subject. Ah!"—she caught her breath—"I adore him!"

Before her awed listener could reply, the Baroness moved across the room. The very manner of her doing so, the delicate grace of her step, the reverent poise of her head, suggested a visitor to a shrine. Following her, Betsy opened the door which once led into the marquee and pointed out on the ground a living memento of the imperial occupation. Rising higher than the turf, kept trimmed and watered by the unforgetting old Toby, was a great crown cut in the grass. "His servants made this in his honor," she murmured.

With a cry the Baroness knelt down. Cupping it with her hands, she pressed her cheek against the green coronet and tears streamed from her eyes. For some moments she was shaken by sobs. Then in a heartbroken voice came the words, "Defeated, dethroned, exiled—oh, mon Empereur, mon Empereur!"

Tears sprang to Betsy's eyes. Yet she felt a strange exaltation. It was as if she heard a million voices speaking through this woman's lips. Never in all the pictures her fancy had summoned of Napoleon's glory had she imagined anything so moving as the grief before her.

When, at last, the Baroness rose to her feet and wiped her eyes, she said in choked accents, "Dear child, who has been privileged to comfort him, I trust you. Say nothing of this to anyone." She adjusted her bonnet with trembling fingers and added with a sad and plucky smile, "My position is not exactly an easy one at best, you understand."

It was of this woman that Betsy thought first during the wild excitement three months later. She longed to know whether Baroness Sturmer, like everyone else, was condemning Boney and if she had any explanation of the incident. Yet the girl realized such speculations were vain. The more the entire island seethed with talk, the less likely were the foreign Commissioners to express any opinion whatsoever.

Betsy herself was the one to bring the news to the Briars. For she had seen the end of the affair with her own eyes. Not all her knowledge of the plots and turmoil at Longwood had prepared her for so astounding an occurrence. Yet afterwards she could trace the sequence of cause and effect.

All these months the Governor had been pressing the Longwood household to sign the official agreement to go or stay. When the declarations were finally turned in, Sir Hudson Lowe refused to accept them because every signer who swore his willingness to remain had used the forbidden term, Emperor. Fresh forms were then sent out. But when further delays and arguments followed, the Governor threatened to deport everyone in the place except the Bertrands. In doing so, he had accused Las Cases of smuggling letters to England and of communicating with Austria. This accusation was taken by some to throw suspicion on William Balcombe as an accessory. Wasn't he frequently at Longwood? Wasn't all his family friendly to Napoleon? Didn't he have constant free access to outgoing ships?

Hearing such whispers, Betsy had been terrified. But from Sir Hudson Lowe came no sign more definite than a hostile manner and Mr. Balcombe quietly continued to go about his business. The next official act was to list for deportation from Longwood Santini, the valet, Archambaud, the groom, and two other servants. Many people believed that the rest secretly envied them. In her headlong way the girl had asked Dr. O'Meara point blank whether Napoleon didn't long to end the perpetual strife between Las Cases and Gourgaud by asking one of them to leave. But the doctor's reply had been an Irish version of the French shrug.

Such was the overture for this twenty-fifth day of November. The bright heat of the afternoon offered no hint of trouble brewing. With one of the junior officers from the fort Betsy set out to see the Bertrands. The family was now well settled in the new house which the British Government had built on the Longwood estate and the girl was eager to see their quarters.

As the two riders came along toward Huts Gate, they saw ahead of them on the road a number of soldiers. Something unusual about the action of this group must have caught the practiced eye of the officer with Betsy.

For suddenly he cried in excitement, "Miss Balcombe, something is amiss up there! Make haste!" They urged their horses to a trot.

Just as they reached the cottage where the Bertrands used to live, the soldiers, who were now formed in a partial hollow square, marched into the enclosure of the garden. Betsy, reining in her pony, saw in the midst of British uniforms and bayonets two familiar-looking figures. Pale and excited were both the faces which flashed up before her unbelieving eyes, and she recognized Las Cases and his son Emanuel. Simultaneously came her companion's low-voiced warning. "Go on! Don't stop! It is an arrest." The next instant, as the horses trotted around the curve, the whole strange scene was swallowed up.

Arrest! For what? The girl had not long to wait for illumination. On the road near the entrance to Longwood she saw General Gourgaud on his horse. Evidently hearing their approach, he turned around and instantly came to a stop. The others reined in beside him.

"You passed them?" he cried.

"Yes," panted Betsy. "What does it mean?"

With a glance at the young Englishman on the other side of the girl, Gourgaud muttered, "Does he speak French?"

"No. Tell me quickly."

"I know little enough. While I was in my room this afternoon, I saw out the window the Governor and a number of officers cross the lawn toward the house. Soon there was a great commotion of talk both inside and outside Las Cases room. I rushed forth just in time to see him being marched away. In the hall I heard little Emanuel call out in answer to some question Dr. O'Meara was asking, 'We are in great trouble. It is about a letter.' I have not seen the Emperor. So I can only guess. Perhaps some document was found on one of the servants when they were all searched before sailing. Ah, poor Las Cases! Alas, poor fellow!"

Nothing about this tale struck Betsy as being more amazing than Gourgaud's grief. "But you—I thought you hated him so and wanted him to leave."

Gourgaud stiffened. "It is different now. He is in trouble with the enemy. I pity him. I would do anything for him—but *anything,* don't you understand?" With a look of disgust for British phlegm, he dug spurs in the flanks of his horse and dashed through the Longwood gate. He didn't even raise his hat.

Betsy stared after him in a daze. Then to her companion she said, "He knows nothing. Do let us find out what happened."

At Deadwood they turned in toward the barracks. Betsy's escort hailed a passing officer whom he evidently knew and then and there they got the whole story. Already it had been spread about the camp.

It appeared that Gourgaud's guess was right. When Santini, the valet, had been searched, two pieces of satin ribbon were found sewed into his coat. They proved to be letters written in invisible ink—one to a lady of high degree in London and one to Napoleon's brother, Lucien Bonaparte. Count Las Cases' young mulatto servant had delivered the suspicious bits of silk to Santini down at the shore. But later the boy had confessed the errand to his father. The latter, in alarm, had instantly reported the tale to Sir Hudson Lowe. The handwriting proved to be that of Las Cases' son.

As the narrator finished his account, he looked up at his friend and at Betsy. Then he said, "Of course, old Boney is back of it all—the crafty devil!"

That was what everybody believed. Once again all St. Helena rang with the clamor that here were deceit and defiance of the Governor and perhaps an attempt to re-peat the escape from Elba. No man spoke the name of Bonaparte without a curse. William Balcombe was grave and seemed so loath to discuss the matter that Betsy was alarmed and believed her mother was also. All the more amazing were Major Fehrzen's comments on the inci-dent. He dined at the Briars a few days after the arrest and talked to Betsy for some time as they strolled to-gether under the pupul trees.

"I don't defend Boney," said the girl, with a horrified thought of what George Carestairs would say of the af-fair. "I suppose he must have ordered the letters written."

"I doubt if he knew much about the clumsy plot. But suppose he did!" replied Fehrzen with a curious smile. "General Bonaparte is not honor bound to play no such tricks. He made no promise of any kind to our govern-ment and always claims that he owes us nothing but re-venge for treating him as a captive. From the first I had a theory and now many people share it. I believe those letters were meant to be discovered."

"What?" Betsy stopped stock-still. "But why?"

Her companion looked down at her with an expression of delight on his bronzed face. "Betsy, I am always astonished at the manner in which I can talk to you. Never have I met a young lady in England who took the smallest interest in passing events—although they say our great ladies do."

Betsy felt strangely moved by the compliment. George Carestairs, also, thought her unlike English girls, but he regretted the fact. Feeling her cheeks growing hot she cried, "Do go on! I cannot imagine why a plot should be made only to be found out."

"Well, Las Cases was most unhappy at Longwood. Yet he could not honorably refuse to sign the declarations that he would stay with his chief. Even if he had refused to sign, he might have been kept here for months before it was convenient to ship him to Cape Town. Now he will probably be sent off at once. If he cannot make his way immediately to England or the Continent, he will at least be more useful to Napoleon at the Cape than here. He can publish his notes and some of the history he has taken down. That is—provided Sir Hudson Lowe returns them. Las Cases' papers were all seized for examination, but I doubt if anything incriminating is found. The man is too sly for that."

Betsy tried to take in this astonishing explanation. She kept reviewing the occasions when she had seen the Longwood family assembled. It seemed more and more strange that across these intimate glimpses flashed no hint of such plots. Once again it struck her that she had but a child's acquaintance with these people. Napoleon loomed enormous on her horizon. But on his, she was a mere speck that occasionally floated under his vision. The recognition hurt. On the other hand—

Impulsively she caught Major Fehrzen's arm and put her thought into words. "It makes me happy that you feel no change of heart toward Napoleon because of this affair," she said.

"Why?" His humorous mouth suddenly tightened as he patted that small hand.

"Well—you are so fine and true. Your not being afraid to stand up for Boney gives me courage."

"I am thankful I can give you something you want." His voice had dropped low, then it changed. "And courage you will need. For someone will soon be here who looks upon the fallen Emperor with very different eyes from yours and mine."

"You mean—?" Wild exultation sped from her heart to her gray-green eyes.

"Yes," said her companion grimly, "he is returning from the Cape. The Honorable George Carestairs is expected to arrive here in a few weeks' time."

That news dimmed everything else which was said or done all evening. The girl felt herself swinging like a pendulum between joy and anxiety. Impending struggle was certain. For now more than ever would the Ensign believe that any kindly feeling toward Napoleon was treachery to England. Yet surely this was just the moment when no real friend would withdraw from that lonely man at Longwood. Betsy knew that in her place Oliver Fehrzen would stand like a rock.

As she watched the Major finally riding away, the girl asked herself in desperation, "How on earth is this tangle going to end?"

11

BETSY WINS A FORBIDDEN RACE

"Oh, dear me, mother! Look, here comes Dr. O'Meara!"

From the window of her mother's room, Betsy had recognized the rider approaching down the driveway. Her mother, who was adjusting over her brown hair a fresh cap contrived of net, ribbons and lace, came to look over her shoulder.

"So it is. He is doubtless coming to wish us a Happy New Year for Eighteen Hundred and Seventeen. But why do you use that tone? I thought you liked the doctor."

Betsy put her arms about her mother's slim waist. "I do. But—well—mother, do you quite trust him, yourself?"

Mrs. Balcombe bit her lip. "Child, that is not a respectful way in which to speak of your elders."

Her daughter gave her a little squeeze. "It is no use trying to deceive me, mother. I have grown too old for that now. You have been troubled for weeks that he and father have had so many conferences here and up at Longwood. I have observed it in your face every time you hear of them. You are afraid of what may happen."

From the girl's embrace, the other withdrew and stepped in front of the mirror again. "Dr. O'Meara is a generous, warm-hearted man. So is your father. Such qualities expose them to danger from an unscrupulous and utterly selfish person."

Anxiously Betsy tried to fathom the face reflected in the glass. "Do you mean—is it Boney, mother? Surely not! Why—now it's my turn to say, 'I thought you liked him.' "

With sudden intensity Mrs. Balcombe whirled about to catch the girl's wrists in both hands. "Oh, Betsy, my poor child, what has that to do with it? Do not idealize him, I beg. Remember that he is—ah—well—Napoleon!"

Comprehending nothing but the sad disquiet of her mother's expression, Betsy palpitated with startled questions. But at this moment her father came into the room. In a cheery voice he said, "Come and drink a toast with Dr. O'Meara, Mrs. Balcombe. And you, too, Betsy."

"I haven't time, father," she replied. "Jane and I are riding up to Madame Bertrand's for a New Year's call. They sent us a signed card yesterday."

William Balcombe, thrusting his hands into his breeches pocket, gave her a long look. "Does the permit include permission to visit General Bonaparte?"

"No, sir, only the Bertrands."

"Then take no liberties with it, daughter," he said gravely. "Remember that to do so would bring upon me the Governor's disapproval."

The girl gave her instant promise with a glance of concern. Now she knew certainly that her father was uneasy.

Could his official position be in danger—even after his long years of service?

In a different tone Mr. Balcombe was saying, "Since you are going into the Longwood estate, I ought to inform you about certain happenings so that you will be discreet. There is bad blood between Count Montholon and Baron Gourgaud. It actually reached the point a little while ago where Gourgaud challenged the Count to a duel with pistols."

"Oh, father, it isn't possible!" cried Betsy, aghast. "Did they fight?"

"No. General Bonaparte stopped it. Since the incident he has been kinder to Gourgaud. I think he realized he has often been cruel to him."

Betsy stamped her foot. "But General Gourgaud is so easily offended. He must be exceedingly trying—and a bore."

"True." Her father shot her an amused glance which was like a welcome into the adult world. "All the same, Napoleon should not take advantage of the young man's adoration." The speaker strolled to the window, looked out and turned again. "I saw Gourgaud in Mr. Solomon's store in Jamestown yesterday and he was buying presents right and left. Several of them were for General Bonaparte. I confess I was much touched."

"But why was he buying presents now when Christmas is over?" asked Mrs. Balcombe. As she spoke, she took her husband's elbow, and, to remind him of his guest downstairs, gave him a gentle push toward the door.

"Presents for New Year's, of course," replied he. "To the French, les étrennes, as they call them, are far more important than Christmas gifts. You must send up some fruit and wine with the young ladies today, my dear. Have it packed into the saddlebags."

As he and his wife left the room, Betsy heard Jane calling from the hall that it was time to start. And so, with her head still full of questions and her hands full of gifts from her parents, she was presently following her sister into Madame Bertrand's drawing-room.

Never had that household presented so animated an appearance. Vases of exquisitely arranged flowers stood on console tables, bookshelves and the piano. Madame Bertrand looked charming in a loose frock of white silk trimmed with gold at the belt and neck and around the wide scarf thrown over her shoulders. With a happy smile she rose to greet her visitors and, murmuring her pleasure, took from their hands the baskets of peaches and the fat bottle of Madeira. Meanwhile, the children with an outburst of chatter, dragged the girls over to view the elaborate game of blocks and tin soldiers which they were playing on the floor. Even Count Bertrand, as he poured out glasses of wine, unbent into cordiality.

"Voyez, mes amies," cried Madame Bertrand, "come to this table and see the lovely things his Majesty sent over as étrennes this morning."

Set out on a brocaded cloth were wooden toys for little Napoleon, a dainty fan and a box of Piron's creams for his sister Hortense. Of course, the handsome tortoise-shell lorgnette was for Madame and the cloisonné snuffbox for Monsieur. Jane and Betsy examined the display with cries of admiration. But the latter thought wistfully to herself that she would have loved having Boney give her a keep-sake for New Year's.

Indeed, in spite of her enjoyment of the children and of Madame Bertrand's soft playing on the piano, unhappiness tugged at her heart. It was so maddening to know that Boney was there in his house only a few hundred feet away and to realize that because of hateful regulations she could not run over to see him. How could these people stand being interfered with all the time?

Perhaps it was her suppressed longing which made her ear so keen. She was the first to catch the sound of boots coming up the front steps of the house. She sprang up with an impulsive, exultant cry, "Madame, c'est l'Empereur!"

Madame Bertrand's hands fell from the piano keys and she remarked with a little smile, "I wish he had heard you call him that."

The next moment he was there. Count Montholon, in full regalia of uniform and sword, was just behind him. In the rapid, harsh voice, so welcome to a certain pair of ears, Napoleon cried: "Bonne Année, Madame! Hoppee No *Year,* Mees Betsee! Bonne Année, Mademoiselle Jeanne! We have had a promenade. Now we have come for a little music."

Instantly Betsy was tingling with joy. This was like old times at the Briars. She saw that Napoleon's usual gray pallor was tinged with color from exercise and that the twinkle she loved was in his eyes. How good it was, after so much sadness and quarreling to have this peace and pleasure once again!

Napoleon was asking Madame Bertrand to play a new

piece of music which had been brought yesterday on the *General Kid,* a vessel still anchored outside Jamestown. "The song, *En partant pour la Syrie,* mesdemoiselles, came from Paris. It was composed by the Empress Josephine's daughter, Hortense Beauharnais, and I desire greatly to hear it. You, Mees Betsee, are to sing it for me."

Madame Bertrand had already placed the sheet of music on the rack. Yet she seemed to hesitate. Finally, however, she began very softly to play and Betsy, standing beside her, hummed the melody.

"Bien, I thought you would have practiced it when I sent it over yesterday!" cried Napoleon from his post across the room. "Play it! Sing it! Commencez!"

Obediently the performers began again. Betsy let her voice soar into the romantic air:

> *"Partant pour la Syrie*
> *Le jeune et beau Dunois*
> *Venait prier Marie—"*

But now, when pressed by a firmer touch and as the notes climbed higher, the piano strings twanged with discordant half-tones and it was impossible for the singer to hold the key.

"Mon dieu, what is the matter?" came the angry voice of the listener. "This is terrible. Can you not play it, madame?"

The Countess sprang up nervously and said in a frightened voice, "Hélas, your Majesty, I regret to say that your wishes could not be carried out. As you requested, we asked Monsieur Balcombe to get the Band Master on the

[223]

General Kid to come up and tune the piano. It seemed so very fortunate that he had arrived, for no one else knew how to do it. Mr. Balcombe arranged everything and the Band Master was most willing. But I presume Sir Hudson Lowe had to be informed of the matter. For just as the musician was coming down the ship's ladder, an order was sent from the Governor that he was not permitted to come ashore."

"Ah, diable!" roared Napoleon, bringing his hands together with a sharp clap. "That cursed hangman! That petty-minded jailer! He would deprive me even of a little music. Sacré Bleu! The Governor is a tyrant for whom England ought to blush. Mon dieu, what a person! Do you know what he is?" Striding over to Jane who was standing near the window, he shook his fist under her terrified nose. "He is the sort of man who would somehow employ cunning in saying Bonjour!"

Count Bertrand was looking mournfully at the ground. Montholon was nodding his head vigorously. Madame Bertrand, with a hand at her slender throat, bent before the storm like a reed in the wind. But Betsy, unlike her shrinking sister, felt an unholy delight in this tirade. It seemed a perfect expression of her own rage and disappointment over the ruin of a charming hour. As for that last characterization of Sir Hudson Lowe, it drew from her an irrepressible laugh.

Startled by the sound, Napoleon turned around and took a step toward her. She met the fierce challenge of his look, by saying impulsively, "Bon, monsieur le Général, you are a wit!"

Instantly his face softened and his anger vanished. A

smile flickered over his lips. "Come, Betsee, let us leave these four to play Riversi or whist. Come with me across the garden and receive your étrenne. Also Piron has made some creams which I shall give you."

He seized her hand and made for the door which the little Bertrand boy sprang to open. Thrilled at the idea of a gift, delighted to be the means of diverting his wrath, the girl followed him gleefully. For an hour her happiness was unbroken. Napoleon took her out to his kitchen to show her the wonderful ice-making machine which had been set up there. He even forgave her stupidity in failing to understand how it worked because of her wild excitement to be touching ice for the first time in her life. Piron, grinning from under his tall chef's cap, stuffed her with creams. Best of all, however, was the wonderful gift Napoleon had selected for her from among his dwindling possessions. It was a beautiful Sèvres cup painted with marvelous art. The picture represented the Emperor in the garb of a Mussulman.

After thanking him in her prettiest French, Betsy turned the cup round and round to scrutinize it. Then with a burst of her former, unrestrained curiosity, she said, "Monsieur le Général, how could you ever pretend to adopt the Mohammedan faith in the East? Do you really not believe in God?"

"What are you saying, little fool?" A look of wrathful contempt was bent upon her. Nor did it soften when tears of hurt sprang into her eyes. "Political alliances have nothing to do with true beliefs. Who told you I was an atheist? Whoever did is an imbecile."

Folding his arms, he gazed into space and the girl

almost forgot the sting of his rough reproof in the interest of watching him. After a moment, with unchanged expression, he went on thoughtfully, "Religion to most people means the church. I care nothing for any church and would gladly adopt the one preferred by whatever country concerned me. For all churchmen are hypocrites. But, on the other hand, Betsee, only a madman denies the existence of an all-powerful Spiritual Force. Every close observer of nature knows we live among deep mysteries— called God."

He turned upon her his unfathomable eyes. Now he patted her cheek. It was dismissal. For he was obviously tired. But it was a friendly gesture and in his face was content—as if, after all, he had been glad to put in words what he thought. She bade him good-by with a rushing sense that no experience could compare in richness with an hour spent with Napoleon.

Not until the lackey opened for her the outside door of the entrance room did she remember. But one glimpse of the distant sentry's bayonet transfixed her with shock. Her promise to her father! She had seen Napoleon without a permit. Now what would happen? Even as the fear smote her, one of the guards came out from behind the wall and looked fixedly at her. He would report this to the Governor. Her pass would be checked and then— Oh, how could she have forgotten her father's interests so completely? She was a wicked, wicked girl.

Even the relief of confession was denied her. When she and Jane returned home, Mr. Balcombe was not there. He was away the entire evening. Even next morning, although Betsy had slept so little all night, the doze into which she had sunk after dawn held her fast until too late. Her mother, who came to wake her, reported that the head of the house had already departed.

"He was wanted at the Governor's," said Mrs. Balcombe serenely. "Perhaps about General Bonaparte's desire to sell some of his silver plate through your father. Oh, Betsy, I do so wish I might afford to buy a piece or two. Think of possessing something which the history books will mention!"

Her daughter did not see her shining eyes. Violently the girl had flung herself back into the pillows. What if Sir Hudson Lowe would dismiss the General Purveyor—disgraced through his daughter's fault. She would die of shame and grief.

That was a morning when she tried the soul of poor little Miss Breen. Betsy was still required to do a certain number of lessons every day. And, although the governess was not much more than a sounding board for the information her pupil unearthed, she did attempt to prevent waste of time. Over and over on this occasion, she had to remind her charge that she could not study by gluing her eyes on the driveway. When at last William Balcombe's figure appeared, Betsy needed but half a minute to be down on the lawn.

With her hand on the bridle of his horse, she cried softly, "Oh, father, what happened? Did you tell the Governor it was all my fault—that I promised and forgot? I have been half dead with fright."

Never had she seen her father so pale and grave. He spoke only with an effort. "It was rather dreadful, Betsy.

Sir Hudson Lowe no longer trusts me. I imagine after this I shall be closely watched."

They stared miserably at one another. Then he gathered up his reins. "Well, we will keep this from your mother. She is not strong and must not be alarmed."

Sinking down on the steps of the veranda, the girl said to herself with a fresh pang of tortured conscience, "He never blamed me—nor even asked my promise not to disobey him in the future!" Of course, at the moment, Betsy was more sure than of her own heartbeats that his trust would never again be betrayed. Yet three months had not passed by before she was carried away by another impulse.

That period in the affairs of St. Helena had been unusually calm. True, battles were still waged by Napoleon and Dr. O'Meara against Sir Hudson Lowe. Often William Balcombe came back from Longwood saying that Boney flung himself into the details of the squabble with a passion worthy of a European campaign. Nevertheless, since the departure of Las Cases there was less trouble and people no longer raced about to exchange gossip. Moreover, Lady Lowe steadily gained popularity. When she sent to Madame Bertrand a box of lovely baby clothes at the time of little Arthur's birth in late January, everyone applauded her magnanimous spirit.

In return Madame Bertrand uttered a quip which was enjoyed even by the Governor's champions. When she first carried her infant son into the presence of Napoleon, she had said, "Sire, I have the honor to present to you the only individual who has ever entered Longwood without the express permission of Sir Hudson Lowe."

Report had it that Sir Pultney Malcom laughed im-

moderately over the witticism. Certainly it was often repeated at the small gatherings on which the islanders
once more depended for amusement. Lately no official
entertainments had been given. At tea parties only the
presence of the International Commissioners and of the
officers in bright uniforms indicated that this great rock
of an island, rearing up out of the sea, held a place of first
importance in world affairs.

To Betsy Balcombe, however, these ten weeks after
New Year's moved at a fast pace of happiness. For
George had come back from the Cape with the air of a
changed man. The very first time they met, the girl let
go her fear of his attitude. Immediately after his arrival
Major Fehrzen had brought him to the Briars for tea. As
they greeted one another, she was conscious both of the
Major's sharp scrutiny and of observation from several
others. Yet the Ensign conveyed to her the sense that they
were completely isolated in a magic world of their own.

Carrying her hand to his lips, he gave her a radiant
look of joy and excitement. "Lovely, lovely Betsy! Lovelier than I remembered!" That was what he breathed too
low for anyone else to hear. Then, straightening to his
full height, he said clearly, "Upon my honor, Miss Betsy,
it is good to be back again."

When he sat down to drink his tea it was beside her.
Yet he adroitly managed to include the group in talk
about his travels and still give Betsy special messages.
She believed that one of his first remarks to Mrs. Hodson
was really meant as assurance to her.

"I found after I left here, ma'm," remarked Carestairs
with genial lordliness, "that on St. Helena I had really

come to like a woman of spirit. The officers' wives whom I met in Cape Town do nothing but embroider and gossip and sit at whist. Here you ride, shoot and play in theatricals. I must say I consider it admirable."

In this harmonious fashion Betsy and the Ensign renewed their relationship. He neither mentioned Napoleon nor any of the events which had occurred during his absence. They saw one another every week—sometimes oftener—and, although they seldom got off quite by themselves, the fact that they were together at the same tea table or on a picnic down at Turk's Cap Bay lent glamour and excitement to the occasion.

George could pack one look with sufficient ardor to make Betsy quite dizzy and he found innumerable ways to tell her of his increasing infatuation. Only one of these methods failed to give her intoxicating joy. She did not like his always coming to carry her off when she was dancing or talking with Oliver Fehrzen. Once, in order to interfere, he walked straight away from Lady Lowe's daughter, Charlotte Johnson. Such was the young man's possessive air that it was small wonder people began to couple their names with smiling significance.

Doubtless these wise folk were responsible for his being invited to Sandy Bay toward the end of March. When Mr. Doveton's daughter planned a supper party for a dozen young people at Fairyland, she was probably told who would be the most acceptable escort for Betsy Balcombe. Since Carestairs had not seen Sandy Bay until then, Betsy had the joy of showing him all its strange beauties—its caves and coves and wonderful jeweled rocks.

Perhaps the unearthliness of the scene affected the young man's mood. He was the silent member of the gay group which explored and climbed about on that unbelievable shore. Over and over he tried to check the auburn-haired madcap with him. He gasped when she made a perilous leap across a narrow chasm and refused to let her scale one of the rocks which, smooth as obelisks, shot upward from the edge of the sea. Finally, he managed to separate her from the others. They sat side by side on a wide, moss-covered ledge of rock watching the long light play upon the restless sea.

"Betsy," said her companion, "you must not take such risks. One misstep in this place and—Lord! My heart stands still to think of any ill befalling you. Look at me! Don't you know how precious you are to me?"

His arm went around her waist and he leaned his cheek against her hair. In silence she watched an eagle alighting high above them. She knew that if George bade her climb with him on its back, she would do it, glad to fly to the world's end.

Presently he spoke again. They were close enough for her to feel the deep vibrations of his voice. "I will soon be able to ask you—to tell you something. I await only an answer to the letter I sent home. Oh, bewitching Betsy, if only—"

He broke off at the sound of voices calling. Peering over the edge of the giant boulder, Betsy waved a hand. "We must go," she said to George. They stood up, and as he held out both his hands, she laid hers in them and they exchanged a grave look which was a wordless pledge.

[231]

The chief topic of the supper party that evening soon became the chief topic of all St. Helena. The races! They were to be held on the Deadwood plain early in April and competitions were offered to every man, woman and child who could ride a horse and had a horse to ride. The stewards were Sir George Bingham, Sir Pultney Malcom and Major Fehrzen. Betting was to be allowed. Prizes were offered various events. In short, here was the most universally interesting affair ever promoted in this midget sporting world.

Betsy thought of nothing else all week before the great day. She intended to enter for the jumps in the ladies' class. One by one she tried out every horse in her father's stable. Peter, the stableman, was highly excited to have his little Missie compete and eagerly put her through the practice. First, she took low barriers of brush which Peter set up in the meadow. Soon she was sailing over walls and hedges. Before the week was up she and Peter together decided that, old as he was, Tom, the white pony, jumped the best and was the steadiest of the lot.

Although Betsy had never even seen a race, she was counting on George to coach her in the rules of procedure. Often he had told her of the local events he had entered as a boy and the races he followed whenever he was on leave. Twice he had had to break appointments with her because of unexpected duties. But at last the conference was definitely set for late afternoon the day before the Turf Club races. To avoid a clutter of people they arranged to meet at Major Harrison's cottage near Huts Gate.

As Betsy donned her riding habit, she felt tingling

with anticipation of the morrow and the joy of the coming meeting. She always delighted in this particular costume and after she had put on the beaver hat and tucked in the last curl, she blew a kiss to the radiant image in the glass. At that instant her eyes beheld another face behind her in the shining mirror.

She whirled around. "Father, how you startled me!"

Her nervous laughter was stilled by the look of grave disapproval bent upon her. "Yes, I suppose so," said Mr. Balcombe. "With your mother and Jane off to Plantation House, I am sure you thought the coast was clear. Where were you going, miss?"

She dropped her eyes. "Riding," she murmured.

"With George Carestairs?" As she made no answer her father went on, "I have just learned how often you manage to meet this man. Betsy, I forbid you to go. Even in these wilds a girl of your age has to obey certain rules of conduct."

"Oh, father, what do you mean? I have never seen George alone. What have I done that you should speak like that?"

Mr. Balcombe turned his eyes from the blushing, pleading face. He spoke in an unfamiliar, harsh tone. "I find it humiliating in the extreme to be taunted by friends and acquaintances about my harum-scarum daughter. Evidently talk about you has reached the point where I am actually asked if you are betrothed to this young scion of a noble family. Inasmuch as Carestairs has not approached me with the least hint of his intentions, I can only judge he is amusing himself at your expense."

[233]

Betsy had grown very pale. "But George—I think—oh, father, I am sure he really cares for me. I remember now he told me he had written his family. Doubtless that is why he has not—why he has to wait. For an answer, don't you see? Indeed, he is the very soul of honor! Everyone says so. You are not fair!"

William Balcombe laid his hands on his daughter's shoulders and now his voice was very tender. "Dear child, I have not realized that you are really grown up. But if now you have a woman's feelings, then you must face facts. We think little of such things here, but—I believe I must warn you that Lord and Lady Carestairs are not likely to consider you a good match for their son. They know neither you nor your family and I, a mere government official, am a poor man. So do not let your heart become involved, I beg you! You must not see this man again. For he will never be allowed to marry you."

Betsy stared. Marriage? She had never really thought about it. She had just been happy. Even now the word held little meaning for her. Yet she felt a deadly power in her father's words. They seemed to be raising up a wall between her and George. An insurmountable wall! But not to see him again was impossible. A sort of fury rose in her that her father should even speak those words. She turned her back upon him and walked to the window.

He followed close behind her. "Betsy, turn around. Tell me this fellow has not made you care for him!"

The girl made no move. Stormily she was asking herself why it was a parent's right to spoil one's happiness. At the touch of his hand on her arm, she flinched and shrank back. She had hurt him. He was moving away.

But still she could not turn around. Then from the doorway came his voice again, loud and authoritative.

"Remember, Betsy, I forbid you to leave the Briars today. Miss Breen has complained lately that you do no work. Your head is full of nonsense and I am not going to allow it. You are to stay right here and prepare your lessons for tomorrow. Otherwise, I shall not permit you to go to the races."

The next moment she heard his feet go thumping down the stairs. The girl stood motionless with her forehead pressed against the cool window pane. Her perfect father! How could he have become such an enemy all in one moment? Sneaking in upon her that way—like a spy —without warning! Telling her she could not see George, not go to the races! How absurd for him to treat her like a child. Lessons, indeed! It was too much. She would not submit!

Through the scarlet haze of her anger, her father's figure came into view on the lawn below. She saw him mount his horse and ride away. For a few moments she stood quite still to gather up rebellion and recklessness. Then, in a whirl of voluminous skirt, she flew down the steps and out to the stables. Peter had a horse saddled for her. Not Tom. They were saving him. Soon she was trotting out the side gate and up the narrow mountain pass which served as a short cut to the Huts Gate road.

Until its very end, however, there was little comfort in that stolen meeting. Betsy felt too wretchedly self-conscious to enjoy it. When George, with a youthfully excited air, rushed to help her dismount, she refused to do so. There wasn't time, she said, because she had to be back so soon.

Disappointment made him stiff. "If you have come only for instructions about the races," he remarked, "here they are." He thrust a paper into her hand. "I have written them out."

For a few moments their keen interest in the next day's prospect kept them talking eagerly. But the weight on Betsy's heart oppressed her. She could not help staring moodily at her companion. Was he just amusing himself? Only as she started to return did she feel anything of their old closeness. Then George stripped off her glove, pressed her hand against his cheek and murmured an endearment. When he said laughing that next day he meant to bet his all on a certain young lady on a white pony, she leaned down a glowing face. He was irresistible. There was nothing she would not either do or endure to make him proud of her.

Would she even lie to her father? That was the question that haunted her as she picked her way down the perilous path. She had never done so. With trembling knees she walked from the stables to the house. But she reached her room without meeting anyone. In the hall she had heard her father's voice in the study, but he did not come out and she was dressed for dinner by the time Jane and Mrs. Balcombe returned. Triumphantly she rejoiced that her disobedience had not been discovered. But, although he asked her no question, Betsy found it hard to look at her father.

Next morning, however, she wakened thinking only of the races. Sleep had blotted out anxiety and guilt. Hurriedly she set off to the paddock to see Tom. What a moment it would be—taking that double jump at the end of the course which George had described! How thankful she was for the clear, cool weather. There would be no mud to make the pony slip.

In the doorway of the stable Peter stood watching her approach. Just as she was wondering why he called no greeting she saw that his face was black with some terrible news. Her voice shook as she asked if something had happened to Tom.

"Yes, missie," replied Peter in a tone thick with emotion. "Even if it is Mr. Balcombe hisself that did it, I feel downright bad. Pity it is that all your hard work has to go for nothing!"

Clinging to the doorjamb for support, she told him to go on. Brokenly he told her. An hour ago Mr. Balcombe had come to the stable and ordered one of the boys to ride Tom down to Jamestown. He said the pony was to be loaned for the day to the French Commissioner who was riding him up to the Deadwood races.

"I said all I dared," groaned Peter. "But Mr. Balcombe declared you would know why he had to do this. God A'mighty, Miss Betsy, you won't even be able to see the races now—let alone compete! There will not be a horse for you left in the stable."

Without a word Betsy walked away to a sheltered spot in the garden. There under the low branches of an orange tree she dropped prone. So! Her father had known of her meeting George and this was his revenge! They would all go and she would be left. How utterly helpless she was. Nothing and nobody would rescue her. The picture of the long afternoon before her brought such unbearable anguish that she sprang to her feet. Surely one chance remained! Her father might relent. Feverishly she rushed back to the schoolroom. She would do her lessons as never before. Miss Breen would praise her and the dreadful punishment would not be given.

But Betsy had not accurately gauged her father's feeling. He made it clear in their interview after luncheon. "Your laziness at lessons is bad enough," said he with quiet sternness. "But worse was your deliberate disobedience. Most improper of all is your willful insistence on behaving as no well-brought-up girl ever behaves. This affair with Carestairs must cease, Betsy. Now and at once! I have given you good and sufficient reasons why. Reflect upon them this afternoon and see if you can come to your senses."

She did not watch the others go. But after she was sure that nobody was about, she strolled forlornly down to the empty paddock. She wanted to be near her only friend, Peter. Innocent as he was, she knew he was being punished, too. He was standing with arms akimbo staring up the mountain path which she had taken yesterday. As she drew near, he turned and she saw that his face wore a curious excitement.

"Look, missie!" he cried. "What do you make of that?"

Approaching down the slope she saw a horseman. It was Dr. O'Meara. And behind him—what was coming? He was leading a horse—a beautiful gray Arabian horse and on its back was a lady's side saddle and housings of crimson velvet embroidered in gold. Betsy's throat seemed to burst with the cry which left her lips. "Boney! Boney is sending me a horse for the races!"

It was true. Laughing at her wild delight, the doctor explained how it happened. General Bonaparte had inquired of Mr. Balcombe that morning if his little Mees Betsee was to enter one of the events. When he heard that her white pony had been loaned and that she had no horse to carry her to the races, he made up his mind to rescue a maiden in distress. This was the very best horse in his stable and Madame Bertrand had provided the saddle.

For just one instant did Betsy hesitate. "Did Boney know why my pony was loaned to the French marquis?" she asked.

But O'Meara had only laughed and told her to hurry into her riding habit or he would not wait for her.

"Come what may, come what may!" sang Betsy to herself as she fastened buttons with trembling fingers. "If I should win the race father would forgive me and be proud. So would George. Boney will protect me somehow —bless him!" Just below her triumph and excitement lurked a deadly fear of consequences. But she could hold it at bay—she must—until afterwards.

Not even on the night of Colonel Bingham's ball was Deadwood so marvelously gay. Everyone on the island was there. Uniforms and hunting coats worn by the men vied in color effect with the costumes of the ladies. Flags were flying. The stewards' box was draped with bunting. Men were dashing about to place their bets. Somewhere the regimental band was playing. Up and down the rough-laid racing course grooms and stable boys were

leading blanketed steeds. As she rode slowly around to the
place where the contestants were gathering, Betsy said to
herself that to be here was worth any penalty—even
another night in the rat cellar.

Suddenly a figure sprang out of the crowd and stood
at her stirrup. It was George Carestairs and his face had
never been so filled with excitement. "Thank God! I was
getting so anxious!" he cried. Even when she had to dismount and let a groom take her horse to be judged and
entered, the Ensign did not notice that she was not riding Tom. He was too much absorbed in his own emotion.

"Darling, I want to tell you something—before you
enter the race. It is bound to bring you good luck. Come
here out of the crowd a bit. I must have a word with
you."

Everything was happening so rapidly. The eager face
before her seemed to waver out of a sea of color, of noise
and movement. Yet the moment he began to speak in
that low, intense tone, the whole scene was blotted out.
Never so completely as at this instant had their magic
isolation closed them around. George had heard from his
family. They had absolutely refused to consider his proposing for the hand of a girl of whom they had never
heard. But now he knew how much he cared for her.
For the answer made no difference. He was going straight
to her father. Tomorrow! He would ask for her hand and
they would be betrothed. "Yes, Betsy," he cried triumphantly, "you can thank your stars you are a pretty witch
or I should never have risked your winning over my
father. Oh, darling, I am so happy that at last I have

made up my mind. I simply must have you and that's a fact."

The girl did not stop to weigh this speech. She felt only bliss to learn how much her lover cared. They stood so close that had they been in one another's arms, they could hardly have been more united. Without even touching his hand, she gave him an endless look from her inmost heart of joy. He had changed the world. Now everything was right. Her father would forgive her. All she had hoped was true. George loved her beyond all others. They would be betrothed. What else on God's earth mattered now?

Someone called her name. An officer with a paper in his hand came rushing up. He said she had to mount her horse and take her proper place. With just time to send George a farewell smile as he shouted, "Good luck!" she walked swiftly away with her conductor.

From then on episodes occurred and dissolved like scenes in a dream. Figures came and went near her. The other women contestants looked at her curiously, stared at her horse. Racers came thundering toward them down the course. At last, however, she and the others at a signal moved forward to the track. They edged into place and Betsy felt the docile gray gather himself eagerly together. Not until that instant had she really reckoned with what she was doing. She was not even sure the Arab had ever jumped. Yet she felt no fear. What if he brought her down? Not death itself had any meaning now. George had told her that he loved her!

A pistol cracked! They were off! The course lay just as George had sketched it. From the corner of her eye

Betsy saw that it was lined with people perching on chairs and ladders, sitting their horses and standing close to the ropes. The first low hurdle was taken without her feeling a change in the pace of her horse. Archambaud, he was called, after the banished groom. Betsy loved him, patted his neck as they flew. Up and over again! The gates were taller now. Beside her sounded the click of hoofs on wood as other ponies barely cleared the barriers. But not the gray! He jumped clean every time.

At the last hurdle she leaned forward and cried his name. Could he do it? For one instant she knew the blackness of terror. Then he landed softly, certainly and as she sped onward, she glanced behind her. She was far ahead of all the rest. Only three horses were over the last gate. A bell clanged furiously. She had won!

Cheers rose up like rockets around her. The entire grandstand foamed with waving handkerchiefs. Major Fehrzen was leaning from the box to shout her name in triumph. As she came to a standstill beyond the tape, men came running up from all directions. Still unbelieving, she sat there patting Archambaud's wet neck. To one of the officers in the enthusiastic crowd about her, she replied, "Oh, it wasn't I. It was the horse!"

As she spoke, two faces appeared over the shifting shoulders of the others. To each her victorious happiness fled unafraid. It was a good omen to see George and her father side by side. Not until she heard his voice, cracking with anxiety, did she see how white-faced and grim was William Balcombe.

"Betsy, whose horse is this?"

Yet the dream state in which she lingered still kept her

from remembering all this meant to an official of the British Government. Proud and swift and loud enough for many ears was her answer. "It's Boney's glorious Arab, father! Dr. O'Meara brought him down from Longwood for me."

Upon her wrist she felt her father's savage clutch. But something else hurt more. It was the sight of all radiance fading from George Carestairs' face.

12

"DO NOT LOOK BACK, BETSY!"

"Sir Hudson Lowe is busy at the moment, Miss Balcombe, but he will see you presently." Major Gorrequer bowed politely as he spoke. Then his boots padded softly across the polished floor of the small reception room.

Betsy watched him go. His tread, like his smile, reminded her of a pussy cat. He would be present, of course, at the coming interview. Dr. O'Meara had told her that the secretary was always there, taking notes on the bitter conversations between the physician and the Governor.

Nervously the girl arose and tiptoed to the window. Out in the beautiful gardens of Plantation House Lady Lowe in a floppy hat was directing a black boy as he snipped fuchsias for a bouquet. A flash of yellow wings came and went among the rose bushes and the sweet sharp trill of a wild canary added sparkle to the freshness of the sunny morning.

It should have been bleak and rainy, thought Betsy, to match the heaviness of her heart. How did people meet catastrophes such as the one which had happened to her yesterday? She would never be the same again—not even if George overcame his loathing of Boney, not even if she could persuade Sir Hudson Lowe not to blame her father. For no one could suffer such anguish of mind and not change.

Except for Major Fehrzen she hadn't a friend in the world. He had carried her off to receive the prize and later borrowed a horse for her and brought her home. He was so proud and pleased. He could not understand the horrible weight on spirits which should have been soaring. Nobody in the family had come near her. True, she had gone straight to her room to sink into an exhausted sleep and this morning had left long before the others came down to breakfast. But as she lay awake in the evening listening to voices below, she had felt waves of accusation wash up from the floor and through the walls.

"Ready now, Miss Balcombe." Again Major Gorrequer stood in the doorway. Again, as he held aside the portiere, she was conscious of his mysterious smile. Oh, now if she could only keep knees and voice from shaking.

Sir Hudson Lowe was standing beside his desk. He had never looked more august. His thin lips murmured her name and his freckled hand waved her to a seat.

Betsy wet her lips and said in a low tone, "My father does not know I am here, sir."

"Ah?" The Governor sat down at his desk and turned upon her a mirthless smile. "I understand that Balcombe's ignorance of your whereabouts, Miss Betsy, is by no means unusual."

The sarcasm acted as a tonic. Instantly Betsy's wan cheek flushed, her eyes glinted with temper and nervousness was replaced by determination. In brief, clear sentences, without sparing herself, but also without mentioning the important factor in the case—George Carestairs, she explained how she had happened to ride a horse from the stable of General Bonaparte. Since it was in direct defiance of her father, it would be most unjust to hold him responsible for broken regulations.

Sir Hudson Lowe listened motionless with his pale brows hiding his eyes. As she concluded her plea, he sprang up and, motioning to the secretary, went to a bureau in the far corner of the room. With their backs turned, the two men murmured in monosyllables and Betsy heard the rustle of papers. The sound terrified her. Did they keep records of everything in the world? Was her father down in their black books?

At last the Governor came back to lean against the desk. Folding his arms, he gazed down in silence at his visitor. Rather than look at his face, the girl fixed her eyes upon the ribbon and gold medal about his collar. She recognized it as the insignia of a Knight of the Company of the Bath and suddenly recalled how magnificently Boney had stormed when he learned that Sir Hudson had been given the rare honor.

"Miss Balcombe," said the dry voice, "perhaps, as you confess, your father knew nothing of this latest outrage against discipline. As a patriot and official, he should, indeed, have objected to his daughter's receiving from a prisoner of the British Government so flagrant a favor as the loan of his horse for a public race. What interests me is why you bring this matter before me." With a jerk of his lean body, the Governor said sharply, "Is it because Dr. O'Meara himself brought the animal down to you? Is it because you know how anxious your father is that his close association with the Irishman be kept quiet?"

The questions were daggers piercing her with doubts. Was her father really combining in some way with Dr. O'Meara to serve Napoleon's interest? The Governor had something definite in mind. In a flash she remembered her mother's anxiety about the same subject. Oh, how little she ever knew what really went on among older people! She felt as if the ground under her feet had yawned. But the eyes shifting quickly from her face and back again warned her to be self-controlled and wary.

In a small voice she asked slowly, *"Is* he associated with Dr. O'Meara, sir? How is that?"* Encouraged by the Governor's look of disappointment at her evasion, she hurried on. "I came because I wanted you to know the truth and not think my father condoned my taking the horse, Sir Hudson. I thought you might understand that to me the loan of that lovely Arab was only a little kindness from a friend. Ever since he was at the Briars General Bonaparte has—well—liked me, sir. I cannot get used to having everything so different now that he is at Longwood. But my father has tried to make me obey the rules, I do assure you."

There was little more to the interview. But at its end the Governor commanded Major Gorrequer to ride back to the Briars with Betsy. Not until afterwards did she learn why. The Major was so casual and pleasant with her all the way that she did not dream he had had to act as a sort of spy. But he could only report back to his chief how thunderstruck William Balcombe really was to learn where his daughter had been and why.

Her father told her all this in the long talk they had that day. His final comment in a grave but friendly voice was, "Well, Betsy, you did your best to repair your damage to my reputation. It was a brave act to go to the Governor and I think it will help."

She had not dared ask him to explain Sir Hudson's insinuations. And of George Carestairs they said nothing. Until he made some sign, the girl could not bear to speak of him. Was he still loving her in spite of his family's disapproval? Surely her riding Boney's horse was not enough to make him give her up! Yet, wretched days went by before she learned from her father that the Ensign had asked permission to call.

"He spoke only of seeing you, Betsy," said her father significantly. "An innocent request which I have granted. A lover in earnest, however, would have wished to have an interview with me. I beg you to tell him once and for all that his attentions must cease."

Betsy received the Honorable George in the summerhouse where once she had learned about war from Napoleon. A few climbing roses still in yellow bloom offered a perfect background for the peach tones of her full silk frock and the auburn warmth of her hair. But one glance at the cold sternness of the face he presented upon entering the enclosure told her the effect was lost. Passionately she wished he had not come. And she was almost relieved when with his first look at her she saw the ice turn to fury.

"You want to make this as difficult as possible, don't

you, by presenting the picture of lovely innocence? But you know you dealt me a fatal blow that day at Deadwood. I cannot forgive you. All this time I thought you had stopped seeing the Corsican—had really given him up for my sake. A-ah!" He lunged a step toward her. "God knows you look beautiful. You look as if you could love a man. But you don't know the meaning of the word. You would give up nothing!"

Even in his rage, the perfection of his features, the grace of his body and the proud strength of him held glamour for her. Wasn't he saying in a queer, topsy-turvy way that he wanted her to love him? He couldn't have come up here just to quarrel. The girl stretched out her two hands as if to reach him through all this cloud of misunderstanding. But Carestairs flung farther away and glared at her over his epaulette.

"How could I come and ask for your hand after that scene at the races? Everyone talking about you! Calling you 'Boney's Favorite'! Faugh—that velvet saddle told the whole regiment whose horse you rode. I blushed for your boldness. Ah, no! The woman I marry must have some regard for my principles."

A dam which had been strained too long burst now in Betsy's heart. "And what of my principles?" she demanded with flashing eyes. "Is friendship nothing? It is important to me. I think there is such a thing as personal loyalty, too. Boney was my friend before I knew you."

Seeing the furious protest in his eyes, she rushed on. "It is not true that no patriot can admire Napoleon. Major Fehrzen does and nobody could question his patriotism. Lady Malcom does. Dr. Warden certainly did.

Every visitor who touches these shores longs to meet him. He is the greatest person I shall ever know—even if he was our enemy. You are too prejudiced and petty to feel that, so you misjudge everything. I should despise myself to refuse to see Boney or accept his few favors just because you object so meanly. It is you who are stubborn and unreasonable. Have I no right to my feelings?"

They were drawn up now for a final battle. Blue eyes and green eyes met stormily. "Rights?" he repeated with a kind of amazement. "It is a woman's right to be guided by the man she loves. You do not really love me. That is what I see."

"But—but—" The girl broke off with sudden despair. They could never get this straight. It was no use. "Oh, George," she cried piteously, "it isn't that. I—I do—I have cared for you. Think how happy we were!"

For an instant the young man looked as if he could have snatched her to his breast. Then bitterness altered his face. "You don't love me enough to make up for the risk I was ready to take. I offered to go against my family, perhaps wreck my chances—be disinherited."

Betsy stared. Now she remembered what her father had said about her not being a good match. She didn't understand that yet. "If my father were rich and had a title, would it make a difference?" she asked wonderingly. "Could I be friends with Boney in that case?"

He flung out his arms in a gesture of hopelessness. "You want to put me in the wrong. You refuse to see. No, we could never—Betsy, we are not suited to one another. You are not like an English girl. You are too self-willed and spoiled. We should never agree!"

[250]

So it was over. All the magic fled. They were staring at one another across a chasm. Betsy felt as if the world were ending. Yet over the pain in her heart was a film of rage that he could let this happen so unworthily. It kept her from sinking to his feet. "Good-by," said she and, drawing back, swept her hand toward the entrance of the little bower. "Please do not come again."

A startled look fled over his face. Then it blurred into something she could not fathom. For an instant he wavered. Then with a half-bow, not superbly this time, but with a strange aspect of defeat, he went out and down the grassy slope.

Some time later, as she lay sobbing in the rustic chair, she felt two strong arms around her. Down came her hands and she looked into her father's face. He was kneeling beside her and his voice was full of tender triumph.

"You turned him off, my girl! Good girl, I know it. I saw him go. Laugh, little pet, do not weep for him. He is not of stuff you really want, for all his handsome face. When the true lover comes, you will see the difference." He drew her head down to his shoulder. "That man will be sure of his own heart and will make you just as sure."

There was comfort in this image. Betsy lay still a moment to reflect that perhaps life were not over for her yet. After all she was only sixteen. The girl in the story book she had read last year did not consider herself an old maid even though still unmarried at twenty-two. When she felt her father stir uncomfortably, her head came swiftly up. She snatched his hand.

"Father, I have been a wicked daughter to you. And

you have been so good to me. All this time you have not said a word about punishment."

William Balcombe stood upright and bent upon her a small, dim smile. "Ah, poor child, it is punishment enough to grow up."

After this Betsy tried her best to keep from thinking of George Carestairs. But all too often she thought of nothing else. The trouble was that interest in him had wound like a creeper around every event. When hoof-beats thudded on the driveway, she instinctively looked to see if the rider wore an Ensign's uniform. If she went somewhere on a party, she trembled for fear he might be there and felt that it was dull without him. Often she thought that without the companionship of Oliver Fehrzen, who seemed in unusually high spirits these days, she could hardly have survived.

Consequently she was doubly glad to receive one day an invitation from Napoleon. He had asked to see her and Sir Hudson Lowe had signed her pass. She was to have luncheon afterwards with Madame Bertrand. There, at least, she would have nothing to remind her of George Carestairs. The June morning when she set off was cool with the promise of the winter season just beginning on St. Helena. It was perfect for riding and the girl felt lively enough to wave to the sentries posted here and there on heights above the road. She felt rather important, too, when she handed in the signed card to the guard at the Longwood gate.

The soldier smiled as if he knew who she was. "The orderly officer says Boney needs a bit of cheer, miss," he whispered. "The General hasn't been out riding lo this long while."

At the door of the entrance room Marchand greeted her somberly. "His Majesty has felt indisposed for some days, mademoiselle," said he. "He is not in the house at present, but in the garden somewhere. Do you wish to wait in the library?"

"Merci bien, I shall go find him."

"Non, mademoiselle, s'il vous plait. He desires to be alone. He heard the signal gun announcing that the *Conqueror* has been sighted. That ship brings the new Admiral to replace Sir Pultney Malcom. I think the Emperor is watching for it."

"Then I shall watch with him." Off tripped Betsy before the major-domo could protest further.

Quite well she knew where Napoleon must be—on the rise of ground behind the Bertrand house. From that point one had a view of the water. Sure enough, as she came around a thicket of thorn trees, she saw him. His figure on the crest of the knoll was outlined against the sky—the tall boots and white small clothes, the old green coat and tricornered hat. In one hand was a field glass. The other was thrust into his waistcoat.

Why did the sight of him standing so make her stop and catch her breath? She had seen him look the Emperor, the courtier, the general of supreme genius, but never had she beheld this aspect. Even from such a distance, the man gazing out to sea, to the far horizons of the world, had an air of indescribable sadness. He must be the loneliest man on earth. Here beneath the clouds stood Napoleon the exile.

It was long before Betsy could summon courage to approach that motionless figure. When she did so, she was abashed before the look he turned upon her. She was an intruder—unwanted. It was a terrible mistake to have ventured. Neither of them spoke. But just as she was turning to flee, he pointed outward beyond the last towering crag. There—with white sails curved to the wind, glad and free and triumphant—sped the *Conqueror*.

For an instant fraught with emotion, they watched together in silence. Then Napoleon's eyes met Betsy's and she knew that now he was glad to have beside him a young and friendly creature. "How would you describe that sight?" he asked in a husky tone.

She thought a moment. "Last year I saw quoted in a review a verse by an English poet. I shall say it slowly, monsieur, and perhaps you will agree that Byron has pictured that ship exactly. 'She walks the waters like a thing of life.' "

When she had repeated the line more than once, while his lips moved in silent translation, he nodded. "Oui. C'est bon. I like that, ma petite."

Sometime later, after they had watched the *Conqueror* around the point, both of them were seated side by side in the garden on a fallen log. They were eating the oranges which Betsy had brought in her reticule. Still grave, but willing to chat, Napoleon told her how sorry he was that many of his soldier friends like the good Captain Poppleton were so soon to leave the island. When in surprise the girl asked him why, he stared.

"Has no one told you? The Fifty-third Regiment is ordered off. Another one is coming soon to take its place."

Betsy turned her head away to hide her start. So George Carestairs was going. She would never see him again. This was a strange new twinge in the old familiar ache.

Napoleon laid his soft hand upon her arm. To her utter amazement, as if her intimate thoughts had been spoken aloud, he said, "I know, Betsee. He is departing —your Ensign. But it is better so. He is an aristocrat and should wed himself to one. You would never have been happy with him. The English snobbism is a terrible thing."

Giving her no time to comment or protest, he suddenly assumed the lively tone of former days. "Never have I had an opportunity to felicitate you, mon enfant, on your victory at the races. You looked well on my horse. I was proud of my little Betsee."

"But"—she looked her astonishment—"but, monsieur le Général, you did not see me, did you? How could you?"

He chuckled gleefully. "When you go to Madame Bertrand, examine the shutters of the entrance room. They are pierced with holes to fit these field glasses. No one can see me then, but I can see much. Yes, yes, I watched the races." He laughed. "I won a gold napoleon on you from poor Piron. He thought you were too fond of sweets to jump well. But zut! My peepholes are a secret."

Still in this cheerful vein, Napoleon discussed the costumes of the ladies gathered that day at the races. Lady Lowe was especially handsome. Baroness Sturmer was equally gorgeous. Poor Madame Bertrand, who could not attend, was very jealous because the Countess Montholon was there. But she had been very nice about lending the saddle for Betsy's Arabian steed. It was a great joke on his friend Balcombe that the latter's little daughter should have entered a race and won, after all, in spite of his prohibition, wasn't it so? Had not Betsy enjoyed it? Why had she never thanked him for helping her win a prize?

Betsy sounded the teasing eyes so filled with lively malice. "Why, monsieur le Général, surely you know what terrible trouble I was in because of that horse. The Governor was very angry. He believed my father was to blame and that it had all happened to break rules and annoy him."

A burst of harsh laughter greeted this remark. "Ah, oui, oui, oui! I know. I was very sorry Balcombe was in trouble. But it was good news that the cursed, assassin of a Governor was angry about it."

Betsy sprang to her feet and clenched her hands to keep down her fury. Boney had not been thinking of doing her a kindness that day, but of how to make more mischief! It was plain to her now. Just as her mother had said, this man was unscrupulous and selfish. He would use a loyal friend for his own ends—even for the petty purpose of irritating Sir Hudson Lowe—without a thought of consequences. For an important design he would not hesitate to send that friend to ruin. What if he were really involving her father and Dr. O'Meara in something serious!

Napoleon had risen also and was strolling toward the house. Suddenly he turned back, came up and seized both her hands. She saw upon his face one of its most sincere and tender expressions, veiled in sadness. "Goodby, leetle Betsee," said he gently. "I rejoice that you came this day. I shall not see you soon, for I receive

few people now. My indisposition seems to increase. I beg
you to pray, with the others, that it may make a speedy
end of me."

Her startled cry of instinctive protest was quenched
by his leaning to kiss her, first on one cheek and then the
other. Then swiftly he strode away.

For a long time the girl stood still. In this one hour
Napoleon had rent her heart with pity, filled her with
suspicious fury, amused her and at the last brought her a
sense of his tragic fate. What was he really? Perhaps, she
reflected, it would take her a lifetime to find out. But
now, standing in his garden, with his voice still in her
ears, she could feel but one emotion. For she was facing
something which had always been shrouded before. Here
in Longwood, shut in by grim mountains, his doom was
written clear. There was no escape for him but death.

At luncheon Madame Bertrand might have been struck
with her young guest's unusual quiet, had she not been
regaling a piece of news. Had Betsy learned of the arrival yesterday of the great Lord Amherst back from his
mission to China? Had she also heard of the splendid
breakfast the nobleman was giving on his ship tomorrow?
Ah, but she would hear, Madame Bertrand assured her.
Invitations were being sent out now. It would be a delightful occasion.

In surprise the girl looked at the heightened color, the
air of coming to life again, which thought of a little
sociability had brought to the melancholy face of the
Countess. How starved for it she must be!

For her own part, Betsy felt she had been through altogether too much to have any heart for a party. Yet next

day, when the time came to go, when Jane was filling the upstairs with gay commotion while one maid ran to borrow Mrs. Balcombe's pomade and another helped to select a bonnet from the array spread out on the bed, when from below sounded impatient shouts from Major Fehrzen and Jane's pet officer of the moment, when old Sarah came in to put finishing touches on her little Missie's toilette, and Mrs. Balcombe, laughing in spite of her headache, arose from her couch to tell them to hurry —well, then it was quite a different matter. Then a mood, bright as the trumpet flower at the window, seized upon Betsy and shook from her all that was not as merry and careless as any sixteen-year-old girl should be.

It was a great lark to be crowded with the others into the ship's longboat at the landing steps. All Betsy's special friends were spilling over the sides—old and young, from Rose Legg and James Bennet to elderly Mr. Doveton and the tart little Miss Mason. As they sped over the glinting rollers, Betsy told Major Fehrzen how she used to go out with her father to visit the brigs anchored in the roads and learn from travelers about the wars. "That was before Boney came, when I was quite a little girl," she said. Whereupon, the Major with something new in the friendliness of his eyes asked her if he seemed to her very old. She denied it in surprise.

To Betsy as to everyone the memorable feature of that party was the host himself. For weeks afterwards nobody could mention the name of Lord Amherst without an outburst of praise. Toward the end of the luncheon Betsy herself started this ball to rolling. She looked across the table set up on the quarter-deck, a table trimmed with the flowers Lady Lowe had brought in a great basket, and heaped with fruits and cakes and decanters of sparkling wine. Watching the handsome head of the diplomat, as he bent to listen to what Lady Malcom was saying, Betsy murmured her impression to Major Fehrzen.

"All the adjectives that belong to him begin with the letter A—like his name—Aristocratic, able, affluent, admirable, amiable—"

"Stop!" cried her companion. "It is my turn. Think of me. I am Oliver—openhearted, omnipotent, original, obliging!"

In the midst of their subdued hilarity, Betsy winged him a glance of gratitude. For two solid months she had not felt so light-hearted. How grieved she was that so good a friend had to be ordered away! But straight to someone else, named George, this train of thought swept her on. It was a cold clutch at her heart. But colder still was the sensation she felt as something made her turn her head just then. There, leaning on the rail, as if he were one of the ship's officers, was George Carestairs himself and his eyes were riveted upon her.

At that instant the signal was given for the guests to rise. As Betsy pushed back her chair, a girlish figure rushed up behind her and bent down. It was Lady Lowe's daughter, Charlotte Johnson. "Do me a favor, Betsy!" she said softly. "Come with me below a moment into the mate's cabin. I have something to tell you."

Glad to escape that apparition at the rail, the girl sprang up and followed her guide. Nor did she stop to wonder at this unusual request until they reached the cabin.

It was very near the foot of the steep stairway and as they entered the tiny place, she glanced curiously around its spare and ordered emptiness. Seating herself on a stool, Sir Hudson Lowe's stepdaughter said with a queer, sly smile, "I shall wait here a bit. But do step into the passage and see if anyone is coming."

Wonderingly Betsy obeyed. Hardly had her feet carried her over the threshold when she found herself confronted by the very figure from which she had fled. In the semi-darkness of the narrow corridor, George Carestairs seemed to tower above her. She shrank back, but he caught her by the arms and drew her some distance from the cabin door.

"I had to see you once more, Betsy," he murmured thickly.

"But what are you doing here?" she whispered. "You were not at luncheon." She felt almost afraid of him. He did not seem the same young man whose image she had been trying so desperately to erase.

"I came to pay my respects to Lord Amherst. He is a friend of my father. But never mind that. I could think of no way to say good-by to you. We leave tomorrow. I may never see you again. I asked Miss Johnson to connive and we arranged it so. Ah, Betsy, I cannot seem to forget you! I wish—you must—Betsy, give me one kiss to remember!"

But this was no humble plea for indulgence. Before he had ceased speaking, his arms went around her in a crushing embrace and she felt his lips on hers. How often she had longed for this supreme moment! Yet now she felt only repelled. To lure her into this shadowed place and snatch what she would never have granted—oh, it was base of him!

With all her lithe strength, she pushed him away until he stood at arm's length, grasping only her wrists. "I hate you for that!" she panted. She felt she had been kissed by a stranger. Now she saw what had never been clear before. Always it had been his imperious will which triumphed. Never had he tried to consider or please her or win her favor. Yet he had told her that she did not know the meaning of love.

For a long moment they stared at one another. The Ensign muttered, "Oh, I can't let you go!" and once more tried to pull her toward him.

Just then, far down the passage, the voice of a sailor bellowed some order and Carestairs, startled by it, relaxed his grip. Instantly Betsy sprang out of reach. Then she turned to meet his last despairing look. She saw him put both hands to his face as if he would blot her out of his mind. Then slowly he stumbled down the corridor. After his retreating shape she flung her scorn in two words, low and distinct, "The Honorable George!" Without a backward glance he disappeared in shadows.

Betsy stood still for an instant. Why had Charlotte Johnson played this scurvy trick upon her? She must have known—everyone knew a thing so marked—that she and George were no longer friends. At once all Betsy's rage focused on the other girl. Two steps to the cabin door revealed that Charlotte still waited within, waited to laugh no doubt or make some silly jibe. Quickly from outside Betsy banged the door and turned the key.

"Let this teach you not to set a trap again for me!" she

shouted and began to mount the stairs. Below she heard a hand beating on the panel, but only climbed the faster.

On deck she saw at a glance that all Lord Amherst's guests were gathered at the other end of the ship and that some were already taking leave. She started toward the group, then stopped to collect her wits. "Ah, the clean, salt wind! Let it blow!" she cried silently. "How good it feels! How free!"

Before she looked around again she heard close by a deep voice, half anxious, half teasing. "Betsy Balcombe, where have you been?"

Now as if for the first time she looked at Major Oliver Fehrzen. He was too rangy and tall for elegance. His deeply tanned, irregular features with the wide, humorous mouth held no claim to male beauty. Yet this man had a long list of virtues she could name. She had tested every one. How blinding the glamour of one personality could be! She heard his voice take on concern as he asked her what had happened to make her cheeks so scarlet and her eyes so full of storm.

"I have been tricked!" she burst out.

The quick sympathy in his face made nervous tears start to her eyes. Whereupon the Major tucked her hand into his arm and said with cheerful firmness, "Come! I must go back now and I mean to take you with me. Most of the small fry have started in the longboat. Now we notables will take our leave of Lord Amherst."

In the genial grace of that distinguished presence Betsy caught a dazzling glimpse of the great world. How remote and small St. Helena must appear to such a being—significant only because of its celebrated exile. Betsy told

Lord Amherst shyly she would love to hear of his adventures into the mysterious interior of China. With a courtier's air he replied that so pretty a head as hers must hold mysteries far deeper and more enchanting.

Thus in a lively flurry of compliments and good-bys the last of the party climbed over the ship's side and down the ladder into the heaving dory. Betsy was so busy keeping her flounces out of the water in its bottom and her bonnet from blowing off in the breeze that the little boat was well away from the ship's side before she noticed who were the other passengers.

Then behind her she heard Lady Lowe's incisive tones. "I presume, Count Balmain, that Charlotte got off ahead of us. It seems odd she didn't wait for you."

At this Betsy twisted round with a cry of such distress that all heads turned her way. "Oh, ma'm, I forgot your daughter! We must go back! Charlotte is on the ship, in the first mate's cabin."

"Vat eez zat?" cried the Russian Commissioner.

"In the mate's cabin?" echoed Lady Lowe. "Charlotte? How utterly absurd, Betsy. How do you know? She wouldn't linger there. She must be ashore."

"No," wailed Betsy. "She *is* in the cabin, ma'm. I locked her in."

Then, indeed, the whole boat was in an uproar. Charlotte's mother demanded explanations. Count Balmain ordered the coxwain to row back to the ship. Other people shouted that they must be landed first and he go back alone. His friends began to take him to task for proving so neglectful an escort for the young lady. Then, as the oarsmen imperturbably swept the human hubbub shoreward, Lady Lowe's voice drowned all the rest. "Betsy Balcombe, you are a little hoyden! This is unforgivable!"

Once again the culprit felt that stab of fear now grown familiar. Would her father suffer for this, too? "But, ma'm," she stammered, "you don't know! Just ask your daughter why I turned the key."

Almost immediately then the boat was edging in to the landing steps and amid much laughter and shrieking the ladies were handed out. The moment her feet touched firm ground, Betsy seized Fehrzen's arm and began to hurry toward the Marino.

But Lady Lowe caught up with them. "Will you kindly explain this conduct, Betsy?" she demanded angrily.

Then Major Fehrzen turned and in pleasantly spoken words put her to utter rout. He suggested that probably a private interview with her daughter would be the course fairest to Miss Johnson, whose offense Betsy was too generous to reveal.

Not until they were on their horses, starting toward the Briars, did Betsy question her defender. Then, with a radiant look of gratitude, she asked, "But why were you so sure that Charlotte had been offensive? I told you nothing."

Oliver Fehrzen said heatedly, "Your perturbation later told me much. Besides, just before the luncheon ended, I had seen her whispering with George Carestairs and looking hard at you. I knew that if you saw him, it would be painful to you—that is—am I right, Betsy, in believing everything is over between you?"

The look of deep anxiety with which he asked the

question changed to satisfaction as she answered, "Everything."

Suddenly the Major laughed. "I take wicked delight in thinking of one of the Governor's family behind lock and key. Oh, Betsy, what an imp you are! And how I hope you will never become sedate!"

She looked at him with a fresh sense of the fun they had together. "When I become sedate, you will be lordly," said she and in laughter felt an old wound begin to heal.

When they had passed through the Briars' gate, the Major asked her to dismount and walk with him down the driveway. Gravely he told her that she was the only reason he regretted leaving St. Helena. He had loved every moment they had spent together. "But somehow," he concluded with his endearing grin, "I feel we are to meet soon again. Perhaps in England."

"England?" she echoed. "How could that be?"

He was leading both the horses. Their reins were in one hand and his other arm was crooked to make a rest for Betsy's fingers. Now he stopped and looked at her as if he wished to convey a meaning beyond speech. "Betsy, I think a man so generous, quick-tempered and warmhearted as your father cannot long endure the narrow policies of Sir Hudson Lowe. The Governor is a petty tyrant of the most stupid sort."

As she sounded his eyes intently, he gave a gay laugh. "I leave you my opinion of Sir Hudson as a farewell present. Share it with no one, little friend." He urged her forward again. "To my mind there is nothing very noble in being a righteous servant to superiors. The power a man has, whatever it is, must be used for human good or disaster follows. Look at Napoleon! He won by genius the most tremendous power the world has ever seen, yet he forgot his fellow men. Ah, but I thank God I have seen him, felt his presence, heard his voice! There is greatness!"

Fehrzen broke off to drink in his companion's rapt expression. "You have always known that, Betsy. That is one of the reasons why—" His arm contracted to press her fingers close against his coat.

She tipped her head back to see him better under her bonnet's brim. "Why—" she prompted; "you think we will meet again?"

They were at the house now and a small black boy came forward to take the white pony. Major Fehrzen had given a little laugh at her rejoinder. Now he carried her hand to his lips and held it tight a moment. "Yes, put it that way now, at any rate. Betsy, dear, this is good-by—yet not good-by, I hope." With a spring he was in the saddle and, waving his hat, he galloped away.

That conversation, cherished, repeated like a lesson to be learned by heart, served Betsy well in the months which followed. Without its guidance to her understanding, she would have found existence even more bewildering. She was told nothing by her parents, even when she made bold to put them questions. Nor did any gossip come her way. Yet her father's change of manner was enough to prove that something dire was going on. He seldom laughed now and his boyish face grew lined and harried.

Jane declared he was only worried about their mother's health. And, indeed, it gave them all the deepest anxiety.

[266]

"Do Not Look Back, Betsy!"

Dr. O'Meara came to see her, gave her medicine and said the trouble was due to St. Helena's climate. After that pronouncement, there began to be hints from time to time that the Balcombe family's departure from the island was a possibility. Still Betsy, who had been made aware of deeper undercurrents, continued to wonder. Was her mother ill perhaps because her father was in trouble with his chief?

Never, not to her dying day, did the girl find out. She only observed how well the malady served as an excuse for change. Hardly had the old year turned into 1818 when it was definitely announced by William Balcombe that he must take his ailing wife to England. Soon he began to train his successor, the genial Mr. Ibbetson whom all the Balcombes liked. Soon trunks were brought down from garret and loft. Presently, amid a fever of packing and preparations, the round of farewell teas and parties began.

None of this activity seemed very real to Betsy. She could not believe she was really leaving the island. Time after time, between chores and gaieties, she made a round of the gardens and went down to the heart-shaped waterfall. It was like flipping back the pages of her life to visit the spots where she had thought her long thoughts, wept out her griefs and reviewed her childish glories. She could not imagine living anywhere but at the Briars. Whenever she returned from a ride nowadays she would hug old Tom until he snorted in protest. Rose Legg was to have him—her father had promised. She had wanted to give him to little Hortense Bertrand, but it involved too uncertain an effort to obtain Sir Hudson Lowe's permission.

Betsy's Napoleon

It wasn't so unbearable to leave the Bertrand family. For somehow Betsy believed she might meet them again. Perhaps in shining, glorious Paris! But thought of saying farewell to Napoleon made her heart dive into blackness. In nine months she had only seen him twice. Once she and her mother had lunched with him, and once, when she had stayed all night at Madame Bertrand's after the New Year's Eve ball at Deadwood, she had paid him an hour's visit. Both occasions had left her with a melancholy sense of his withdrawn spirit and failing health. To take that final leave, knowing it was forever—how could she face it? It was a relief that her father was going also. He and Jane together might sustain her.

At last the day came. From the moment they entered the Longwood grounds until they left them again, Betsy tried to fix every detail in her memory. In the billiard room where Marchand kept them a few moments, she noticed more maps upon the wall. The great history was still progressing. She had heard that even the major-domo took his turn at dictation these days.

When they reached the reception room, Betsy's eyes flew to the stout figure advancing to meet them. He was heavier and more pale than she remembered. But the silky brown hair, the beautiful features, the smile—these were unchanged. His greeting held the intimate warmth reserved for friends and he kept Betsy's hand for a moment imprisoned in his own while he asked for Mrs. Balcombe and expressed his regrets that she could not come with the others. Then he held out his hands in an eager, beckoning gesture.

"You must come and see what has been sent me by the

Empress Marie Louise. It is now my most precious possession." With his quick, energetic step he led the way into his bedroom.

There on a strip of black velvet over the Pembroke table it stood—the loveliest sculptured head Betsy had ever seen. The purity of marble gave to the delicate features framed in curls a wistful sweetness less boyish than angelic. "My son," said Napoleon in an unsteady voice. "My little son. The bust was sent from Italy."

At the laudations of his guests, Napoleon's eyes lighted. It seemed hard for him to look away from the cherubic head. But finally he asked them to observe beside the bed the pile of books just arrived from the British Government. "At last," said he bitterly, "it has entered those wooden heads that I might like to read. I also have Dr. Warden's book—full of errors, but not bad. I'll show it to you." He stepped over to the mantelpiece and, feeling for the volume, lifted his great felt hat lying there.

He started back. Betsy shrieked. Jane jumped upon a chair. For a rat, a huge, black rat, had run out from under the tricorn, leaped down and, before Mr. Balcombe could aim his boot at it, disappeared.

"Oh, monsieur!" Betsy ran to him and clutched his arm. "How dreadful! It makes me rage that you should have rats here. Can't they get rid of them?" She shivered with the memory of a certain horrible night she had once spent.

"We are overrun with rats. They are everywhere," Napoleon replied morosely. "This cursed house was once a cow-shed, you know, and has no cellar. In consequence, we have rats and damp. It is always damp. I keep a fire burning much of the time."

The three visitors shook their heads sorrowfully. There seemed nothing to say to lighten the dreariness. When they returned to the drawing-room, the gloom increased. Napoleon went to the window and stood sadly looking out. Over his shoulder he asked, "When are you sailing, Balcombe?"

"Day after tomorrow, sir, on the *Winchelsea,* a store ship of the East India Company just anchored today from China."

"Ah, oui. Bien, I may watch it from my knoll—watch you, almost the last of my friends, sail away towards England. You are leaving me on this cursed rock, among these iron mountains which are my prison walls. Be glad, friends, when you hear that the Emperor Napoleon is dead."

He was answered by a strangled cry from Betsy. Sinking into a chair, she burst into tears. Instantly Napoleon was beside her. "Non, non, petite Betsee, do not weep. I shall say no more. We shall try to be gay. Stop, mon enfant, you will spoil your charming eyes." Seeing her grope wildly for her handkerchief, he whisked his own from his pocket and mopped her wet cheeks. "Pull the bell rope, Balcombe!" he cried. "I must order wine and some bon-bons for Jeanne and Betsee."

"I could not eat them, monsieur," sobbed the girl. "They would choke me."

He patted her head solicitously. "Then what would you like for a souvenir?"

She sat up and smiled through her tears. "A lock of your hair!"

"Bon! You shall have it, foolish little one!" To the servant who had answered the bell he commanded, "Quick, bring scissors! I must be barbered to please my little madcap." As the servant with shocked face approached him with comb and scissors, Napoleon said with feeling, "I shall remember always the great kindness of the family Balcombe. We have spent pleasant hours together, is it not so?" With a courtly bow, he presented to Betsy the wisp of dark hair folded in a scrap of paper.

And so the last farewells were said. Napoleon clapped William Balcombe on the shoulder, embraced Jane, then Betsy, kissed each on either cheek. At the door Betsy turned for one last look. He waved his hand. "Do not forget me, leetle monkey!"

Forget him! Two days later, standing at the ship's rail beside her father, Betsy Balcombe looked back at the receding shape of St. Helena. Cruel and strange, it dashed upward against gray stony clouds. Behind those volcanic walls, behind the frowning line of guns, was a little man in a green military coat, guarded from dawn to dawn by a hostile world.

"Father, do you think Boney is watching us go?" Betsy choked.

William Balcombe looked down at her anxiously, but his tone was round and firm. "No, darling. He has forgotten us already in the interest of his memoirs or a new quarrel with Sir Hudson Lowe. Betsy," he went on, "I have not told you yet. Yesterday I had a letter from Major Oliver Fehrzen."

"Oh, father, did you? What did he say?" She was all alert attention.

Her father uttered a happy laugh. "He said that he is in England and will see us soon." The speaker put his hands on his daughter's shoulders and whisked her around. "Do not look back, Betsy. Look out there where the sky is so bright. That is where we are going—toward the future!"

AUTHOR'S NOTE

This story is based directly and closely on the memoirs of Mrs. Abell, who was Betsy Balcombe, published in England by James Mowatt in 1844 under the title, *Recollections of the Emperor Napoleon During the Time Spent by Him in Her Father's Home in St. Helena.*

Since the truth of the amazing incidents involving the exiled Emperor with the daughter of William Balcombe has been acknowledged by all authorities on that particular epoch, Betsy's Napoleon was apparently a reality and not a fictional view of an historic character. As literally as possible I have represented the real personnel of the island and of the officials and the military stationed on St. Helena from 1815 to 1818.

So complete has been the scholarly documentation of the daily occurrences at the Briars and at Longwood during the residence of the famous prisoner that I feel I must confess my few liberties with historical sequence. For example, the billiard table was not set up so soon as appears in this story. Furthermore, in point of fact Betsy spent New Year's Day at Longwood, not in 1817, but in 1818. Also, Gourgaud falls ill in my tale at about, but not exactly at, the actual time. Finally, although Gourgaud's Diary reports Major Fehrzen's interest in Betsy Balcombe, neither the mercurial Frenchman nor the grown-up Betsy offers any data whatsoever on the progress of her emotional development. Consequently, there is no authentic record of romantic episodes within the pattern of the years which wove this young woman into history.

Even today, however, on that grim and almost deserted rock thrust up off the coast of Africa there lingers the tradition of Betsy Balcombe. It glows in the softened light thrown by time upon the glamorous figure of Europe's terrible warrior. Both the inhabitants of St. Helena, and visitors from every land who stop there, are grateful that across the dark canvas of Napoleon's last years passed one sun-ray—the prankish gaiety of a little red-haired girl who had for the exile a real affection.

JEANETTE EATON.